MW00940282

Two prayers
before bedtime

"Ever has it been that love knows not its own depth until the hour of separation."

Kahlil Gibran

Two prayers before bedtime

NADINE WOJAKOVSKI

FABULAR PUBLISHING

First published in 2014 by
Fabular Publishing
London

CreateSpace paperback	ISBN: 978 0 9930007 0 6
eBook – mobi format	ISBN: 978 0 9930007 1 3
eBook – ePub format	ISBN: 978 0 9930007 2 0

Cover design by Design for Writers
Typesetting and layout by Chenile Keogh

AUTHOR'S NOTE

I did not want my debut novel to be a story about so much sadness and suffering but at the same time I knew that if I ever told a story, this would have to be the first.

About seven years ago my great-aunt Fay told me a fascinating wartime story about my mother and grandmother that I had never heard before. It was then that the title of the book came to me. Shortly after, I wrote the opening paragraph but then found that I could not continue. My children were young and I knew I was not emotionally ready to explore the painful history of this period. Somehow, by the summer of 2013, I was ready to embark on my mission. My fact-finding trip took me from London to Amsterdam and then to Antwerp as I uncovered the detailed history of Amsterdam and that of my family.

The tale/memoir is based on the true story of my grandmother, Cilli Bitterman, and how she and her husband, my grandfather Eugen, had to send their daughter (my mother) Renata and son Arthur into hiding in Amsterdam during World War Two. It also tells of the heroic efforts of Vie and Aart Versnel, who risked their lives to hide a Jewish child in Nazi-occupied Holland. That is why the book is dedicated to them.

In the book the names of the Bittermans and the Versnels have been changed. As there were so many missing pieces to their personal stories, many details had to be fictionalised alongside the true events that did take place. It therefore did not seem appropriate to use their real names (except for that of Renata who authorised it). It also gave me the opportunity to reflect on how many people lived and behaved during this time alongside the fateful history of Amsterdam. (The section in hiding and members of the Dutch Resistance are totally fictional, but based on many real stories.)

In the book the Bittermans are known as the Biermans: Cilla, Edmund, Anton and Renata.

The Versnels are known as the Resnels:- Valerie and Arnold.

The "true story in pictures" and the family tree at the end of the book reflect what is true. This should be looked at only after you have read the story so that the ending will come as much of a surprise to you as it did to my grandmother.

I have fond memories of my grandparents and was lucky to have my grandfather at my wedding (he passed away the following month). I look back now at the difficult lives my *opa* and *oma* led and am left in awe at how they managed to stay positive after the war, given all they had suffered.

As I learnt about how lives were shattered in wartime, I began to appreciate my ordinary, daily life even more. Kissing my children good night, saying goodbye to loved ones, sleeping in a bed, walking in the street, sitting in a cafe ... these small pleasures are ones I can no longer take for granted.

Nadine Wojakovski

ACKNOWLEDGEMENTS

Thank you mum for having the courage to tell me what you remembered of your story and thanks to you and dad for your unfailing love and guidance.

Thank you to my dear husband, Oded for your love and support and for always believing in me. Thank you to my special sisters – Miriam and Jackie, and to my beautiful children – Nathalie, Nicole and Alex – for all your wonderful help, advice and support throughout the process of researching and writing this book.

My deepest gratitude goes to Rebecca Bitterman for the detailed and comprehensive Bitterman family tree, information, photos and constant communication. To my great aunt Fay Bitterman, Cilli's sister-in-law – thank you for recounting the fascinating story about my mother which inspired the title, as well as all the other stories about the family.

I am indebted to the professional help and dedication given to me by, teacher, Sharon Footerman, internal layout designer, Chenile Keogh, and the book cover designers, Rebecca and Andrew Brown of Design for Writers. Thank you also to copy-editor, Cressida Downing of the Book Analyst.

For historical information my gratitude goes to Marc de Hay of the Dutch Resistance Museum, Anat Harel and Lonnie Stegink of the Amsterdam Jewish Historical Museum and Maarten

Frankenhuis who was the director of the Amsterdam Artis Zoo.

I am also grateful to the books, institutions and websites that provided invaluable information. In particular:

Ashes in the Wind: The Destruction of Dutch Jewry by Jacob Presser
Saving the Children by Bert Jan Flim
The Promise by Eva Schloss
Never Surrender! A True Story by Liliane Pelzman
And No More Sorrow by Liliane Pelzman
The Heart has Reasons: Dutch Rescuers of Jewish Children During the Holocaust by Mark Klempner
www.annefrank.org
www.hollandscheschouwburg.nl
www.joodsmonument.nl
www.hiddenlikeannefrank.com
www.verzetsmuseum.org
www.jhm.nl

A special thanks to friends Sharon Dewinter, Beth Feingold, Vivian Kestenbaum, Yosi Klein and Diana Rosenfelder for their valued help and support.

A heartfelt thanks to high school teacher Janine Ellerman for reading the book and sharing it with some of her year seven and nine English students. A big thank you to Abigail Eida, Joelle Deutsch, Elianna Levy, Avital Cohen and Michael Kelly for their invaluable feedback. Thank you also to my niece Emmanuelle Benjamin, and to Jackie Benson, Daniela Kestenbaum, Izzy Pactor, Claudia Spencer, Judith Spencer and Dorthe Tate for their valuable input.

Finally, thank you to family, friends and colleagues Amira Bardichev, Tsipora Blog, Shalom and Sylvie Bitterman, Anna Casale, Ingrid de Groot, Eliza Goldberg, Yvette Goulden, Rob Harris of Copywrite, Annabel Karmel, Nicola Loftus, Vesna Majdak, Melissa Shooter, Shelly Simons and David Smith of Memories for all their help.

CHAPTER ONE

Amsterdam: Thursday 17 September 1942

Cilla tucked her head into the collar of her raincoat so none of the late-afternoon people strolling by would see her tears. Blinded by grief, she paused outside the park, gripping the iron gates for strength and wiped her face with her handkerchief. She saw her daughter, smaller and smaller until she faded out of view completely, like a petal floating down a river. Her heart felt as heavy as lead. She found herself panting heavily, her hands shaking. Then she crouched down and vomited. She wiped her mouth and retched again. And then the weeping started again. The young mother hugged her knees, finally careless of the indifferent passers-by.

She turned back to look at the fountain where she had left her infant daughter Renata just moments ago. On the ground lay a small furry object. She strained her eyes and peered intently. There on the gravel lay Renata's teddy bear, the one her grandfather had given her when she was born. Cilla hurried over and picked it up. She brought it to her face, smelled it and squeezed it hard. Her child's last words still echoed painfully in her ears.

"Don't go! Stay, mama. Stay mama, mama ma ... ma, ma ... ma!"

CHAPTER TWO

Wednesday 16 September 1942

C illa sat huddled on the sofa, her face buried in her lap.
Her husband Edmund was staring out of the window.
The view was picture perfect. The pretty street was
lined with imposing lush elm trees. Dappled light from the bright
afternoon sun shimmered on the pavement below. The serene
beauty of the day seemed to mock the fear and terror of the people
below, hurrying urgently, heads down, collars up, trying to be
anonymous in a big city. The invisible trepidation and hysteria
outside had spread indoors, like a gas, into the cosy sitting room
of the Bierman family.

The pretty, immaculate sitting room had once been a happy
place. At a card table by the window, friends had gathered to play
cards and Rummikub. The book shelves were lined with Jewish
prayer books, art books and novels. Beside them was a glass
cabinet proudly displaying gleaming silver. On the middle shelf
stood a pair of ornate candle sticks and a smaller, simpler pair.
The bigger pair was a wedding present from Cilla's mother-in-

law when she got married. Candles were lit every Friday night on the eve of the Sabbath. Only two candlesticks were required but Cilla had added another two, one for each of her children, whom she included in the weekly blessing.

The room had a wooden floor, black marble fireplace and white cornices bordering the ceiling. It was classical and elegant. Theirs was a comfortable existence. Not lavish or grand but stylish, homely and very happy. It wasn't long ago but it felt an eternity since family and friends had laughed, chatted, played and lived in that lively room.

The two children hesitated timidly at the door, then they ran in. Renata, a tiny toddler, jumped on her mother's lap and five year-old Anton curled up at his mother's side, pulling her arm onto his lap. Cilla's face was red, her eyes blotchy, her long dark hair unkempt, her pretty, delicate features no longer visible. In place of her beautiful smile, a look of desolate grief overshadowed her face.

"What's the matter mummy?" asked Anton.

"Nothing, nothing darling," she replied, sniffing and wiping her eyes. The child knew not to press her for an answer. Edmund came over to the sofa, sat next to his young son and held his hand firmly.

No-one spoke for a very long minute. The sound of silence had never been louder. The sense of foreboding never greater.

It was their last night together in their family home on Plantage Parklaan. Tomorrow Cilla and Edmund would kiss their baby Renata goodbye and pray and hope that she would be well looked after – but more importantly – that she would survive the war.

Cilla put her baby to bed very slowly and methodically that

night. Keep it special, she thought, I can't let her see my pain. Moreover, she wanted to "enjoy" and remember every moment together. She played with Renata in her bedroom and recited her favourite bedtime stories. And finally, when it was time for bed, she slowly pronounced the Jewish bedtime prayer, *Shema*, with Renata.

"*Shema Yisrael Hashem Elokainu, Hashem Echad*. (Hear O' Israel, the Lord is our God, the Lord is One.) Can you repeat that after me?"

They practiced it together a few times, first Cilla, then Renata. Cilla urged her small child earnestly never to forget these sacred words, from the most important Jewish prayer.

"We say it every night darling, so don't forget it," she said gently. She then tucked her daughter into bed, kissed her forehead lingeringly and told her she loved her now and always.

"Please let God look after you now and always my precious baby," she whispered. She closed the door lightly, leaned against the door post and closed her eyes.

CHAPTER THREE

Thursday 17 September 1942

By mid July 1942 the war against the Jews of Amsterdam had reached its climax as the *Razzias* (raids) were stepped up. Nazi soldiers sealed off streets and smashed through people's doors with their rifles and Doberman dogs, rounding up as many Jews as they could. The raids could happen any time, any place and without notice. Anyone caught was loaded into trucks like cattle. Final destination: concentration camp. Later the names would become notorious: Auschwitz, Bergen Belsen, Sobibor, Theresienstadt.

The raids had become a regular part of Amsterdam life. It wasn't safe remaining at home and it wasn't safe out on the streets. The Nazis were obsessed with catching the Jews anywhere they could. And, in an effort to maximise the numbers they caught, they offered Dutch people money, initially only five guilders, to catch a Jew. The life of a Jew now had a price. It was valued at about the same as a week's pay for an unskilled worker.

By now, the only way to escape this terrible fate was to go

into hiding. The safest plan for the Bierman family was to send the children into hiding separately. As Renata was so young, she would be easier to place and easier to hide. A home was found for her first. The Resistance contact, a woman code-named Lotte, told Cilla that her colleague, code-named Helga, would meet her at Wertheim Park across the street from her apartment.

Lotte was part of a tight network of dedicated university students who could not tolerate the cruel treatment of the Jews. They found homes for the children, falsified documents and stole ration cards for the hidden children. Lotte's colleague Helga lived in a student house directly across the road from the Gestapo headquarters. On the night of a big raid she heard trucks pulling up, dogs barking and hysterical screaming and crying. She looked through her window and saw Jewish men, women and children being dragged out in their pyjamas. They were beaten and kicked before being forced into the trucks. Helga was devastated. Later when someone approached her and asked if she wanted to work for the Resistance, she did not need to think about her answer.

The sun shone through the window of the child's bedroom as Cilla brushed and brushed her dark hair. Renata was chirpy and chatty, excited to go out with her mummy. If Cilla could have just frozen this moment in time she would have been the happiest person in the world. Let the future go away. Let me just stay with my baby in this room forever. She forced the thought out of her mind and continued with the preparations. She pulled her baby's hair away from her face and tied it with a pretty pink ribbon. With her smocked summer dress and little curls she looked a pretty picture. Cilla stared at her beautiful daughter sitting in the little chair, consciously storing up every detail. She surreptitiously pulled some hairs out of Renata's head, smelt them, kissed them and wrapped them in some tissue and put them into her pocket.

In the living room, a few minutes later, Edmund embraced his only daughter tightly, holding her close so she could not see the tears. He removed his round-rimmed glasses as they misted up and rubbed his eyes. Cilla stared fixedly at the silver candlesticks. She said nothing. There was nothing to say. She bent down and picked up the small bag of precious belongings she was allowed to take for her daughter. It included a few essentials: hairbrush, toothbrush, pyjamas, basic clothes and her favourite doll, Kitty. The bag was designed to look inconspicuous. Enough clothes for a night away perhaps, certainly not for an indefinite stay.

Renata left home with her cherished teddy bear in one hand and a bottle of warm milk in the other. She planted herself happily in her pram ready for her adventure.

Cilla stepped out of the building, looking up and down the street. She knew German soldiers did not patrol here at this time of day, but she checked to be certain. She was not wearing the obligatory yellow star on her coat so she had to move quickly. The journey to the park would only take three minutes if she was fast. She pushed the pram down the steps and set off. Usually she found it frustrating not to be able to see her daughter's face when she pushed her on their walks together. Today she was grateful for the blessing. She crossed the road and walked the 100 metres to Wertheim Park. Nervously, she glanced ahead, still fearful of being stopped. No papers and no star. The consequences would be severe. Her heart skipped a beat, her hands were shaking.

How ironic that this very park – in which Cilla had spent endless hours playing and laughing with her children – was the one earmarked for the separation. The park was named after Abraham Carl Wertheim, a well respected Dutch Jewish banker, philanthropist and politician who had lived a century earlier, just one of the many Jews who had helped to make Amsterdam the great and beautiful city it was today. How tragic that his park was now forbidden to Jews by yet another anti-Jewish law.

At the gate she looked out for her contact. There by the fountain, as arranged, stood a young woman in a blue dress and yellow bag next to a man of a similar age. She approached them cautiously. Prudently, she waited till the young woman addressed her first.

"Cilla?"

"Yes, and you are?"

"Helga, and this is my friend Otto,"

"I was not told about him," said Cilla, nervously.

"We decided it would be more plausible if he came. Firstly, I am blonde and he has black hair. Together we look like we could be the girl's – I mean Renata's – parents," she explained.

Cilla's voice cracked. "Where are you taking her?"

"She is going to a good home outside Amsterdam. We are taking her straight there."

"Please can I have their details,"

"You know the rules,"

Cilla pressed, "Please, just a name, something."

"We cannot supply names or addresses. They are endangering their lives Mrs Bierman. We need to protect them as much as possible," replied Helga, firmly but sympathetically.

"So how will I know my baby is safe?"

Helga looked at Cilla. She took her arm gently. "I understand your pain. Please believe me. Your daughter will be safe and well looked after by her new family."

New family! The words burnt into Cilla like red-hot needles. Cilla, the real mother, was handing her daughter over to another "mother" who would in turn hand her over to a third "mother," all in one day. How would her daughter cope? She had longed for this baby so much. She had loved her so much and now she was forced to hand her over like a parcel. She felt sick.

"How can you possibly understand my pain?" asked Cilla bitterly.

"No, you are right. I can't. But I can sympathise with you. And that's why we are helping you."

"Yes, I know. I'm sorry. It's just so difficult for us," she said looking up at Otto too, "and we are grateful."

Helga looked around nervously and saw a couple entering the park, wheeling a pram. A little boy, about five years old, was running at their side. "We need to get going before anyone sees us together."

Cilla bent down and kissed Renata on the lips. The child looked at her mother and lisped: "Play now?"

"No darling, not now. There is no time. Mummy has to go away and aunty Helga will look after you."

Renata looked perturbed. She eyed the stranger doubtfully, "No, just mama."

And I just want you too darling, thought Cilla. But that's not allowed. Not now. One day soon I will get you back and I will never let you go again. Never. You will be my princess forever again.

Her voice faltered, "Aunty Helga is mummy's friend. She will look after you." She braced herself and continued as calmly as she could, "Mummy, daddy and Anton always love you, remember that, ok? ... I love you, we love you."

Cilla turned to leave. Renata started crying, first quietly and then escalating to a shrill, endless howl.

"Don't go! Stay, mama. Stay mama, mama ma ... ma, ma ... ma!"

CHAPTER FOUR

September 1935

Cilla Schiff was born on 23 September 1912 in Kosice, Czechoslovakia. She was a descendant of one of the founding Rabbis of the Jewish Chasidic movement, a spiritual sect of Orthodox Judaism founded in the eighteenth century by Rabbi Elimelech Weisblum, of Lizhensk in Poland. Although her immediate family was not Chasidic, they were strictly orthodox, embracing Jewish customs within their large, tight knit community. Her mother, Miriam, had died when Cilla was very young, so as the only child she took on the task of being the home-maker for her father, a dairyman. She embraced the role with fervour and love and became an accomplished cook and baker. By the time she was eighteen her father had remarried, a woman called Maria Weinberger. The family moved to Amsterdam to embark on a new life there together.

Edmund Bierman was born a few years earlier on 28 January 1910, also in Kosice, but he'd moved with his family fifty miles away to the village of Spisske Podhradie. In 1935, just as he turned twenty-five years old, Edmund was offered a good career opportunity by his uncle Pinkus, a furrier in Amsterdam. Edmund knew a little about the fur business from his father Shaul, who traded preserved eggs for rabbit furs. This opportunity seemed exciting – an offer too good to refuse.

While life in Czechoslovakia was bearable, Jews always felt under threat from the constant undercurrent of anti-Semitism. Moving to Amsterdam felt like the opportunity for a fresh start. The Netherlands' very existence was based on the right to have freedom of religion so it was an attraction for Jews who were religiously oppressed in other lands.

In the 1930s thousands of Jews from Germany found refuge in the Netherlands and, in particular, Amsterdam to escape the persecution building up against them in Germany, where the Nazi state had introduced more and more anti-Jewish laws. Jews felt safe and were accepted in this beautiful and cultured canal-lined city. It was a city of enlightenment at the westernmost part of Europe and just across the Channel from England.

One beautiful Sabbath in May 1935 Edmund and Cilla were introduced to each other outside their synagogue in Amsterdam. The fact that they were both from Kosice, and spoke both Hungarian and Yiddish, resulted in an instant connection. They chatted in the courtyard in Yiddish, basking in the sun. Edmund was attracted by more than the looks of the pretty, petite dark-haired young woman. She was intelligent, soft spoken and graceful. Similarly, besides being well dressed and good-looking, Cilla found him charming, intelligent and ambitious. After a brief courtship Edmund proposed and she instantly accepted.

They were married in the Rapenburg Synagogue in

Amsterdam in September 1935 in the presence of family and a few close friends. They embarked on their new life with energy and zeal. While Edmund focused on his new work, learning about the fur trade, Cilla was left with the challenging task of finding a place for them to live. It was mid September and the weather was warm and pleasant. The young wife trawled through the vibrant city on her bike, on the special paths designated for the many young cyclists. She passed the barge-laden canals, busy bridges, parks and cafes and marvelled at the colourful townhouses overlooking the canals. The people looked absorbed and happy and their attitude was contagious. She had a spring in her step and was delighted with her new life.

Cilla was especially concerned about the location of her home – it would need to be within easy walking distance of a synagogue – as orthodox Jews were forbidden to travel on the Sabbath – and close enough to her father's home. Taking the good advice of Edmund's uncle and aunt Pinkus and Rachel, Cilla looked in the Plantage neighbourhood, one of the new areas where many Amsterdam Jews took up residence after 1900. It was a pretty, quiet residential area, which also had the benefit of being surrounded by many attractions including a zoo, a botanical garden, a theatre, parks and cafes.

After a few days of intensive searching, Cilla fell in love with a charming second floor apartment at 24 Plantage Parklaan. It was small but beautifully presented. The steps from the street led up to a porch tiled with blue and white mosaics. But it was the living room and dining room that won her over. It was of neo-classic design with original features consisting of wooden floors, corniced ceilings and a black marble fireplace. It breathed a style and elegance which seemed to complement Cilla's own personality. Moreover, the small apartment building was across the road from the Wertheim Park, down the road from Hortus Botanical Gardens and around the corner from the Hollandsche Schouwburg Theatre and Artis Zoo. What more could she hope for?

Edmund agreed that it was a perfect choice and the deal was sealed. They moved in the following week, on 23 September, her twenty-third birthday.

After a day spent dusting, cleaning and unpacking, Cilla was exhausted. With a mug of freshly brewed black coffee in her hand, she slumped onto a box, legs outstretched and a beaming smile lighting up her face. She was tired but elated at the prospect of the new life ahead of her.

Life was good for the newly-married couple. While Edmund was hard at work learning the ropes of the fur trade, Cilla spent every spare moment exploring the city on bicycle. Although she had lived in Amsterdam for several years she had never really got to know the city as well as she should. Finally she felt she had the time. She spent her days exploring the city's rich heritage and in particular its wonderful collections of paintings by Rembrandt, Van Gogh and Vermeer. In the evenings, when Edmund was not too tired, she booked tickets for classical concerts at the neo-classical concert hall, the Royal Concertgebouw or for theatre performances at the Hollandsche Schouwburg Theatre.

The following year, in the spring of 1936, they received an important visitor. Edmund opened the door to a well-built, well-dressed, handsome young man.

"Hello, how can I help you?" asked Edmund.

"Hello Edmund, It's me … Shia."

"Shia? Shia who?"

"Your brother!" he exclaimed.

Edmund looked at him quizzically. The last time he saw his youngest brother Shia was before he moved to Amsterdam a few years earlier. His brother was then, he estimated, around fourteen years old. The man in front of him, dressed in a suit, raincoat and hat, bore no resemblance to the little boy he knew.

"Don't joke with me. Who are you and what do you want?" said Edmund firmly.

"I am your brother, the son of Shaul and Sura Raisel. I am the brother of Usher, Yossel, Beile Freide – and you."

Edmund digested all this information. Could this be him? It was unbelievable. He had made the hugest physical transformation from boy to adult. But yes, there was no mistaking those beaming bright beautiful grey blue eyes. They were those of his baby brother Shia.

The older and younger brothers embraced for a long time. Shia, who was nearly eighteen years old, was working for a Polish bank and was passing through Amsterdam.

Shia stayed just a few days, but forged a strong rapport with his older brother and new sister-in-law Cilla in that time. On Sunday afternoon they walked in the spring sunshine through the parks and streets, soaking up the peaceful hum of activity. For Edmund, who had no immediate family in Amsterdam, the visit was a special time to bond with his "baby" brother, who had somehow, miraculously, become an adult. The roots of a deep, tender bond began to be laid.

Shia's departure was followed by exciting news. Less than a year after they married Edmund and Cilla found they were expecting their first child.

CHAPTER FIVE

September 1937

The smell of fresh chocolate yeast cake wafted through the front room at 24 Plantage Parklaan. Seven-month-old Anton was sitting on the floor. Cilla was sitting next to him, feeding him stewed apples. With his glossy jet-black hair and deep blue eyes, he was a strikingly good-looking child.

"One more spoon darling, you want to grow into a healthy boy," she coaxed. Anton dutifully complied. "Good boy, darling. Now mummy is going to take the cake out the oven. Okay?"

Off she went to the kitchen, her happy singing voice trailing in the background. When she was not speaking to her son, she was often humming a Hungarian or Yiddish folk tune.

It was a Friday afternoon and Cilla was finishing her final preparations for the Sabbath. The dining room table was set with silver cutlery, sparkling glasses and porcelain dishes. It was ready for the evening meal enjoyed every week by her family which always included her father and step-mother. She had prepared the traditional gefilte fish, chicken soup and roast chicken in the morning. Last but not least she baked her famous Kokosh chocolate yeast cake. She had perfected the cake in her childhood home in Kosice but in Amsterdam it had become her trademark. Everyone wanted the recipe and she gave it out happily, but still, no-one could quite make it as delicious as she did. Every week she baked two cakes – one for her home and one for her father who lived nearby.

When her mother had died, many years earlier, Cilla had worried incessantly about her grief stricken father. Seeing him happily remarried and living close by was a great relief. Still a relatively young man in his fifties, he had opened up a milk and butter shop in his home when they moved to Amsterdam. While the new business kept him very busy, nothing gave him more pleasure than to see his daughter, her husband and baby grandson.

Cilla's morning routine included taking Anton for a walk in his pram via her father's home. Come rain or shine, like clockwork at 10 a.m. they would be out and about. She would walk down Plantage Parklaan to the intersection and turn left onto the quaint, stylish Plantage Muidergracht. There on the right hand side was a deep, dark canal, lined on both sides by grassy banks and tall old trees. Sometimes on a Sabbath afternoon she would sit with Edmund and Anton on the sunny banks, shaded by the willows, contemplating the barges. If she was lucky, she would look up and glimpse her father taking a stroll with his wife Maria on the other side of the canal. "Ta-ta!" she would shout cheerfully, to the slight disapproval of others on the bank. They would wave at each other and her father and his wife would come and join the family on the banks a few minutes later.

But on her daily walk she headed straight for her father's

home on Nieuwe Kerkstraat. In his starched white coat, he would usually be serving a line of customers. Cilla would quietly approach in the background, wave at him and wait for the queue to diminish. Often he would call his wife Maria to take over if she was free and then hurry over to greet his daughter and grandson. Father and daughter always hugged each other as if they were being reunited after an interval of months. Then her father would scoop Anton out of the pram and take him to the back of the shop and to the biscuit tin.

As soon as Anton was old enough, Cilla introduced him to the huge, wonderful zoo literally around the corner from their home. The Artis Zoo, built in 1838, was the country's largest and oldest zoo complete with an aquarium and planetarium. The impressive complex, adorned with large eagles over great wrought-iron gates, was a favourite haunt of the young family. Artis was short for *Natura Artis Magistra*, Latin for "Nature is the teacher of art".

The rich vegetation, sprawling grounds and exotic animals, against the backdrop of beautiful 19th century architecture, gave each of them unforgettable memories. Anton loved the giraffes, wild beasts, zebras and lemurs. But the most spectacular sight was the dozen or so pelicans paddling in the water. The ritual was to save the best for last. The family would sit at the coffee shop on the outer decking, overlooking the water. There they would marvel at the pelicans showing off on a bright sunny day, Anton clutching his ice-cream and his parents sipping coffee.

CHAPTER SIX

April 1938

Edmund's career as a furrier, working for his uncle Pinkus, was going well. He had learnt every aspect of the trade quickly and had proved to be an excellent craftsman with a keen eye for detail. He could identify different qualities of fur skins, knew what would sell and what would not, and was a good negotiator. With Edmund's good eye for cut and fashion, the winter of 1937 has been a busy one as many fashionable women came to treat themselves to a luxury coat or stole. But the season was short, and as the winter ended so did demand. It was now a good time to take a well-deserved break.

The young couple decided to visit Edmund's family in his home town of Spisske Podhradie in Czechoslovakia. His mother Sura Raisel, who had been ill for many years, had recently taken a turn for the worse. The timing meant he would be able to spend Passover with all his family. It would also be a perfect opportunity to introduce them to Anton.

They set off for Spisske Podhradie the week before Passover.

After a long and tiring overnight trip travelling across peaceful German valleys and bustling cities they arrived at the quaint town. The following day the entire family congregated at Edmund's family home. But Edmund was shocked at how frail and poorly his mother looked. He was glad her new grandson gave her much needed pleasure as she sat in the armchair, too weak to move.

Grandfather Shaul and Grandmother Sura Raisel cooed at their baby grandson. Uncles and aunts marvelled at his beauty and good nature. Even elderly great grandfather Yaakov, the patriarch of the family, was there to meet his great-grandson.

Yaakov Bierman had grown up in Galicia, the easternmost province of the Austro-Hungarian Empire, where he had run a general store. He attributed his long life to his meeting with the famous Chasidic Rabbi Chaim Halberstam – author of the hugely renowned Bible commentary *Divrei Chaim* – who had many decades earlier blessed the old man with a long life.

Many photographs were taken documenting this memorable trip, dubbed "the royal visit" by the family. A large family photograph was taken. Grandfather Shaul and Grandmother Sura Raisel sat at the centre, flanked on both sides by Cilla, Edmund, and the siblings – older brother Usher, younger brother Yossel, sister Beile Freide and baby brother Shia. In front were Usher's wife Pearl and their baby daughter Gittele. Finally, in front of them, great-grandfather Yaakov sat on an armchair with little Anton on his lap. Cilla was looking directly at the lens, fresh faced and beaming. Later on they went to the courtyard for more photos with the siblings and children.

Preparations were made for the celebration of Passover, commemorating the Exodus of the Jewish people out of Egypt into freedom. The table was laid in all its glory. At its centre was the Passover plate with the symbolic foods connected to the Jews' endurance in Egypt. Bitter herbs, a hard-boiled egg, a lamb shank bone, green vegetable and sweet nut mixture adorned the plate. It was a long night as the family followed the story of the Jewish people's Exodus. Everyone drank the customary four cups of wine, sang songs and ate heartily. It was a memorable and pleasant evening but for the fact that Edmund's mother looked so poorly. She summoned all her strength to get through the long evening but her face revealed that it was difficult. The siblings exchanged anxious looks and prayed this would not be her last Passover. But it was. She passed away that week, on the fourth day of Passover, aged just fifty-two. The festival's celebration was transformed into a period of utter grief. She was promptly buried, according to Jewish law, her family heartbroken at her sudden passing.

Sura Raisel had lived just long enough to see her latest grandson, and was spared the horrors of the invasion of Czechoslovakia which came a year later, shattering the lives of so many Czechs. After the period of mourning, Edmund, Cilla and Anton returned to Amsterdam, grief stricken.

It was nothing in comparison to the utter devastation they were yet to encounter.

CHAPTER SEVEN

1939 – 1940

On 15 March 1939, German troops marched into Czechoslovakia. They captured Bohemia, and established a protectorate over Slovakia. Two days later British Prime Minister Neville Chamberlain delivered a speech saying that he could not trust Hitler not to invade other countries.

Germany's invasion into Czechoslovakia was a shocking revelation for Cilla and Edmund. They immediately considered the possibility of crossing the North Sea and taking refuge in England, where Edmund's brother Usher had moved the previous year with his family. If war broke out, as seemed increasingly likely, this island, they believed would be far more secure from invasion. Cilla convinced her father and step-mother to join them and, after much persuasion, they agreed.

Obtaining tickets and visas was very difficult as demand was at an all time high. Eventually, they managed to secure tickets for a steamer for Harwich leaving from Hoek van Holland. They hastily packed their belongings and said goodbye to friends and neighbours and set off for the port. The mood was sombre as they left the city on a very windy morning. They caught the train bound for Hoek van Holland with plenty of time to spare.

Due to the high winds the train stopped and started frequently. Edmund looked at his watch nervously. At Leiden station, the announcement they dreaded was made – the train could not move till further notice – a tree had fallen on the track ahead. The family panicked. If the train did not resume its journey very soon they would miss the boat. And miss the boat they did. They arrived at the port twelve minutes after the boat had departed, its stern a tiny speck in the distance.

Disheartened and demoralised they returned to Amsterdam. Edmund tried desperately to secure five more places on the next boat but to no avail. The boats were heavily overbooked. He was placed on a waiting list but held little hope for getting his family across the sea this time round.

At six o'clock on the morning of 1 September 1939, German tanks rolled into Poland. Two days later, on 3 September, after Germany had ignored a British ultimatum to withdraw, the headline in the *Daily Mail* cried out "WAR!" It stated: "Great Britain and France are at war with Germany. We now fight against the blackest tyranny that has ever held man in bondage."

After the defeat of Poland, the rest of Europe fell to the Nazis like a pack of cards in 1940: Denmark, Belgium, Holland, France, Norway, Romania. In Amsterdam, life became ever more tense, most of all for the Jewish community, which had heard terrible rumours about the persecution of Jews in Nazi-occupied countries. Entry into the UK was now impossible.

Then came the news that Edmund's youngest brother Shia was volunteering in a Czech unit, stationed in the UK. He had left his home in Spisske Podhradie swiftly, following the remarriage of their father in 1938 after the sudden death of their mother. Shia had worked in the diamond industry, commuting between the Amsterdam diamond exchange and Belgium for the last few years. But now with the war in full force the twenty-two-year-old wanted to help the fight against the Nazis.

Cilla carried on with her life as best she could, so very anxious for what the future held. Then in March 1940 there was more personal tragedy for the Biermans. Edmund's aunt Rachel – his late mother's younger sister and the wife of his uncle Pinkus Friedmann – died suddenly at the age of fifty. Rachel had been a warm and compassionate anchor of support to the young couple. Her death and, in particular, the funeral in the Jewish cemetery in Diemen, outside Amsterdam, took its toll on Cilla. She felt her world was crumbling, caving in, layer by layer.

But this was just the beginning.

CHAPTER EIGHT

May 1940

The Netherlands declared itself neutral in World War Two as it had done in World War One. It believed this was entirely possible as Hitler had promised the country non-aggression. But Hitler had other plans; on Friday 10 May 1940 the Nazis invaded the Netherlands. On the 16 May, following heavy bombing in Rotterdam, they invaded Amsterdam.

That same week Cilla discovered she was pregnant with her second child.

Twenty-seven-year-old Cilla went to the doctor at the end of May. Sitting in the waiting room, she studied the newspapers spread over the coffee table. "Amsterdam invaded," "Rotterdam bombed," "Terror unleashed," "The world at war," read the headlines. By the time she was called into the doctor's surgery Cilla was sick at heart and weak with fear.

Dr Gus was a kind-hearted Jewish man in his sixties. He had moved to Amsterdam from Berlin with many other German Jews in 1933, after the rise of Hitler and the Nazi Party. He had been the Bierman family doctor for the past six years – since Cilla was pregnant with Anton. Dr Gus examined his young patient and looked at her compassionately: "Surely, you do not want to keep this baby?" he asked softly.

At any other time such a question would have been astonishing but given the situation the doctor felt compelled to speak his mind. In fact, as a close friend of the family, he saw it as his duty to warn his patient.

"You must realise that it is far too dangerous to carry a baby during a war, and especially now that the Netherlands is occupied. I came here from Berlin when things were getting bad and now they are terrible there. It looks as if Amsterdam is going down the same road, it just took longer to happen here."

Everyone had heard about *Kristallnacht* (the night of broken class) in Germany on 9–10 November 1938. That night Nazis had burnt synagogues, Jewish stores, warehouses and homes. Since then the persecution of Jews in Germany had escalated to terrible proportions.

Cilla said nothing so he felt duty bound to continue, "Bringing a Jewish baby into this world in this war is mad." Cilla still said nothing so he continued. "I am extremely sorry Cilla but I think you should have an abortion. I know what I am talking about. We don't know what will happen tomorrow never mind next week. You cannot chance it. How will you cope looking after another child? Why put yourself through this extreme risk and danger?"

He had said it and hoped it would have the desired effect, however painful. She listened calmly, tears welling up in her eyes.

Cilla knew that many women would have listened to the doctor's advice because he was certainly right that this was no world in which to bring a child. But she had longed for this baby and she could not ignore the fact that there was a life growing in her womb. Under no circumstances was she going to intervene.

She met his eyes and responded in her own composed manner, "Dr Gus, I appreciate and thank you for your concern, truly I do." She hesitated and took a deep breath before she continued in a soft voice, "I have longed for this baby. It is here inside of me and is here to stay. Please," she pleaded, "I came here to ask you for your help in keeping my baby not getting rid of it."

CHAPTER NINE

June — August 1940

The writing was on the wall for the Jews of Amsterdam. Life very quickly became progressively worse in mid 1940. They were no longer allowed to hold government jobs or own their own businesses. They had to turn in their bicycles, were forbidden to use trams or ride in cars, could only shop between 3-5 p.m. and were not allowed out on the streets after 8 p.m. As time passed, the list of prohibitions continued, swelling to monstrous proportions.

Cilla's pregnancy coincided with a city becoming overwhelmed with terror. Food rationing first began in June with bread and flour and was later followed by tea and coffee. She tried to concentrate on the mission in hand — to have a healthy pregnancy and look forward as much as possible to the impending arrival of her baby. Towards the end of the pregnancy she tried to rest as much as possible.

But with all the bad news coming in, she found it impossible to rest. She had heard that over a hundred Jewish people had already committed suicide in Amsterdam during the first weeks of the occupation rather than face what they suspected the Nazis had in store for them. The others kept a low profile in their depressing existence.

Her close friend Paula Miller came over to see her one evening. Paula had left Germany a few years earlier and had come to Amsterdam precisely because she believed it offered a safe and peaceful life. They had met socially and had become good friends. They were drinking coffee in the front room. The talk these days was only of war.

"But who would ever have believed things could get so bad for us here?" Paula said in bewilderment. "We always believed Amsterdam was a safe haven – that's why we came here."

"Yes, I know. It's like there's no end to this madness. If only the Americans would join in the war, they'd drive out the Germans and the Russians. We think things have become as bad as they can and then we learn about some other prohibition against us."

"I can't take it anymore."

"It's so scary."

"Yes it is! At least no Jew has been murdered here yet," added Paula.

"It may only be a matter of time".

Cilla felt the pain again. She had suffered periodically from stomach cramps following a severe bout of food poisoning a few years earlier. Now, possibly exacerbated by the pregnancy, they had resumed. A few years earlier, when she was pregnant with Anton and the pain had been acute, the doctors had wanted to perform surgery on the abdominal area but she had refused for fear it would interfere with the pregnancy. She suffered silently now, biting her upper lip. The physical pain seemed to mirror the emotional distress all around her. After her friend left, Cilla sat for hours in the dark, contemplating her family's future.

She worried about the impending birth and what was in store thereafter. Dr Gus was right, she thought as tears stung her eyes. She just had not had the foresight to know that then. She wondered: was it courage or stupidity to have this baby? Right now it seemed very much the latter.

Moreover, she deeply regretted that they had not succeeded in getting to England and now there was no prospect of it ever happening. Since the day war had been declared all the borders had closed. Europe's Jews were trapped.

CHAPTER TEN

1941

1941 was a defining year for the Jews as more and more severe anti-Jewish measures were enforced. The most dramatic act was the registration law, passed in January 1941, when all Dutch citizens over the age of fifteen had to register with the civic authorities and from then on carry identification cards. Almost everyone obeyed. For the Jewish people it meant confirming their religion with a "J" stamped on the card. It seemed a harmless bureaucratic irritation; they could never have dreamed that this would help the Nazis carry out their murderous plans so efficiently so soon after.

All Dutch Jews were ordered to move to Amsterdam so they could be contained. "Forbidden for Jews" signs appeared on the doors and gates of cafes, swimming pools, sports fields, museums, zoos, libraries, theatres, markets and many other public places. All associations had to expel Jewish members and Jews were not even allowed to travel without permission. The Nazis stepped up their campaign with the utmost efficiency. Even the pleasure of owning a radio was denied them and they were forced to hand them in.

The Nazis cleverly established a Jewish Council to act as an intermediary between themselves and the Jews. The Jewish Council workers were puppets doing the Nazis' dirty work. They had to convey all anti-Jewish measures in *The Jewish Weekly* so there was no excuse for any Jew not knowing about the latest law against them.

One of Cilla's last outings before her baby was born – and before access to public places was forbidden to Jews – was to hear the music of Czech composer Bedrich Smetana at the Royal Concertgebouw concert hall. In days gone by she would have been thrilled by the prospect of an evening out at the magnificent neo-classical concert hall. Not so on this occasion. As the orchestra played Smetana's well-known *Má Vlast* (My Fatherland) – portraying the history, legends and landscape of the composer's native land, Cilla was mesmerised. She was transported back to her childhood and her home town of Kosice. She had left Kosice to come to Amsterdam, which she had learnt to love in the early years. But now the city of Amsterdam had proved a lost dream.

At the beginning of January, eight months into her pregnancy, Edmund tried to cheer her up by taking her to the cinema, where they saw *The Great Waltz*, an American film based very loosely on the life of the composer Johann Strauss II. It was their last cinema outing before it was illegal for Jews to see a movie. Very soon after the sign posted outside read: *No Jews Allowed*.

Everything that Cilla had learned to love about Amsterdam had now been destroyed. By September 1941, the occupying forces had banned Jews from visiting Artis Zoo or any other "public establishment". Jewish members of Artis received notice that their membership had been discontinued. During this time the Nazis changed the name of Cilla's favourite theatre, around the corner from her home – the *Hollandsche Schouwburg* into the Jewish Theatre. Jewish performers, no longer permitted to appear before a non-Jewish public, now acted and played for an exclusively Jewish audience there.

On the 6 February 1941 a baby girl was born to Cilla and Edmund. A beautiful, healthy 8 lb baby, with a shock of black hair and strikingly-shaped almond eyes was welcomed into this crazy world. Her birth was bittersweet – magical for the sheer miracle of the creation of a longed for human being, but yet so bitter because of the certainty that a terrible future lay ahead.

They named her Renata Raisel: Renata meaning rebirth, a name associated with new beginnings. It was an optimistic choice and perhaps an act of faith in the midst of the panic that reigned throughout Amsterdam and indeed, the whole of Europe. The second name, Raisel, was chosen in memory of Edmund's mother.

Cilla wanted to treasure every minute she could with her beautiful baby for as long as possible. An instinctively kind and caring mother, she showered her daughter with love. She cuddled, hugged and kissed the precious baby. In turn Renata was a great source of comfort to her parents. They were conscious of the dangerous world that had befallen them so brutally and so suddenly, and intended to hang on to every second of every minute of normality that they could with their young family. They knew that each day that passed brought them closer to a fate too frightening to even contemplate.

One Saturday lunchtime, a few weeks after Renata's arrival, Cilla sat in her armchair cradling her new baby. These days her pale face was etched with constant pain and worry. Every week that passed seemed to age her by a year. The once fresh-faced young woman had become exhausted and world-weary.

Edmund returned from Sabbath prayers at the synagogue, white as a ghost. His eyes were red and swollen. She got up instantly, "What's happened?"

"Sit down darling," he said.

She sat down slowly.

"Hundreds of Jewish men have been arrested by the Green Police."

"What," she gasped, "why? What do you mean?"

"We were in the synagogue and all hell broke out outside. The Green Police were dragging young Jewish men to Jonas Daniel Meijer Square. There were masses of them being dragged from the synagogue, streets, from anywhere. I ran on before they could catch me."

Cilla stared at him speechless. She got up and hugged him tight, relieved he was safely home but terrified at what might have happened. Jonas Daniel Meijer Square was just a ten-minute walk away, situated alongside the magnificent 17th century Portuguese Synagogue. It defied belief.

"What about my father?" she suddenly whispered.

"I went by his home just now to check. He's safe. The men who were arrested all looked young."

"But why?"

"I've no idea. Probably because they are Jewish."

What had the world come to? There was no knowing what would be next. Everything was spiralling out of control. Cilla suddenly thought about Edmund's lovely aunt Rachel. She had died just the year earlier and her stone-setting, after eleven months, had taken place just the week before in the cemetery in Diemen. Cilla wondered, cynically, if aunt Rachel was the lucky one. She had died just before The Netherlands had been invaded and she never saw the humiliating persecution of the Jews, and now this. She had been laid to rest with mostly happy memories of Amsterdam. Not so for those she left behind.

Soon the terrible details emerged. The Green Police had cordoned off the Jewish Quarter and arrested young Jewish men, dragging them off the streets, out of their houses or from the synagogue on that Saturday morning.

Ironically, they were rounded up in the square named after the first Jewish lawyer in the Netherlands – Jonas Daniel Meijer – known for his battle for legal emancipation of the Dutch Jews in the 1800s. There the men were marched in columns and forced to run past a gauntlet of policemen swinging their truncheons before being ordered to squat for hours with upraised arms. The following morning, on the Sunday, more men were snatched off the streets and arrested, bringing the total number of arrests to over four hundred men between the ages of twenty and thirty-five years old. The men were deported to concentration camps: Buchenwald in Germany and then to Mauthausen in Austria.

On Monday afternoon Cilla walked solemnly to the grocery store during the restricted hours of 3-5 p.m. as had been imposed by the Nazis. She was deep in thought following the weekend's tragic events. When she arrived her thoughts were interrupted by a howling voice. She looked up to find a middle-aged woman being restrained by two men. She was screaming and crying, her arms flailing desperately.

"My boys, where are they, where are they? They will be murdered, they will be murdered." She repeated the words again and again. She could not be controlled.

A crowd gathered. Cilla was in shock. She asked another onlooker what was happening. A lady in the shop told her that the woman, a widow, had just found out that her two sons had been arrested at the square. She was beside herself with grief. "They will be murdered, they will be murdered."

The words rang through Cilla's ears like a prophecy of universal doom. None of them would escape the net closing around them.

The news of the brutal round-up spread through the Jewish community very quickly. It emerged that this had been in response to an incident in which German-Jewish refugee Ernst Cahn had been held responsible for spraying a German police patrol with ammonia, intended to repel intruders at his Koco ice cream parlour. The event became known as the "Koco Affair". Cahn, who refused to name the individuals who had installed the ammonia canister, was shot by firing squad a few weeks later.

The mass round-up sent shock waves throughout Amsterdam and beyond. The Nazis had shown their hand. What they had started in Germany in 1933 had spread throughout Europe and had now reached the Netherlands. The Communist Party called for a protest strike. A few days later thousands of Dutch workers went on strike, refusing to return to work. But the strike was crushed when the Nazis threatened to arrest and possibly shoot five hundred more Jews. The February strike was arguably the only mass protest over the plight of the Jews during the war.

By the summer of 1941, obituary notices filled the columns of

The Jewish Weekly, for the lost sons, husbands and brothers who had been sent to Mathuasen and would never be returning home again.

CHAPTER ELEVEN

April – July 1942

By the end of April 1942 it had become compulsory for Jews aged six and over to wear the Star of David. The resentment and hatred had built up gradually over the years but now with the yellow star proclaiming "Jew" in Dutch – *Jood* – it was there in full force, official and for all to see and acknowledge. Jews who were caught without the star risked immediate deportation as criminal offenders. This was a turning point in the Nazi campaign for a Jew-free country. From here on in there was no stopping the descent into horror.

Cilla sat by the window, sewing the yellow star on to her coat. Anton walked in. He had just turned five. She felt a surge of relief that he was still exempt from wearing one.

"What are you doing mama?"

"Sewing on the stars on daddy's and my coat".

"Does it have your name on?" asked Anton curiously, as he came up close to inspect it.

"No, darling."

"So what does it say?"

She looked up and sighed heavily. How was she going to explain? "It says "Juud, you see," she said pointing to the letters.

"But why? Is it a star for being good, like my teacher gives me for good work?"

"Mmm, no darling, it's completely different."

"So, why? Who needs to know?" he pressed.

Cilla rubbed her face, unsure what to say next.

"Is it in case you or daddy get lost?" he offered.

If only, she thought. She put the coat down on the floor and drew her son close to her. Her face was very sad, "It's just the way it is … unfortunately."

In the summer of 1942 the persecution against the Jews took a dramatic turn as those, as young as fifteen years old, were being called up for "forced labour" in the East. The Nazis gave the Jewish Council the impossible task of selecting who had to go. On 14 July nearly one thousand Jews were rounded up in Amsterdam Central Station and were taken to Westerbork Camp. Ironically, Westerbork was a base that had originally been set up in 1939 to house German Jewish refugees. It had now turned from a refugee camp to a transit camp. But transit camp to where?

From mid-July the campaign to deport Jews from Amsterdam – through raids and house arrests – intensified. Stories about doors being knocked down, Nazis coming in with rifles and Doberman dogs, people being dragged out in their pyjamas, beaten and arrested became commonplace. Nowhere was safe.

Cilla took refuge in her neighbour Ingrid's tiny patio garden filled with potted plants. Ingrid lived alone and was horrified at the treatment of Jews. In the last few months she had grown very close to Cilla, offering her friendship and support whenever she needed. There was just enough room in the tiny garden for Renata and Anton to play. It was their private sanctuary, the only place left in Amsterdam where they could feel free. Edmund also used it as his place of contemplation. Sometimes late at night he would smoke a cigarette, deep in thought. They cherished these moments of privacy and freedom. But soon they too would disappear.

Cilla rarely went out except to get supplies and visit her father. One afternoon in July, out during the permitted hours for Jews, she went to visit her father. Barely a few streets away from his home on Nieuwe Kerkstraat, she heard the screeching of tyres and the barking of dogs ahead. A raid! Cilla froze. The yellow star on her jacket made her a prime target. She looked ahead. Nazi police and dogs everywhere. She saw them dragging Jewish men, women and children off the streets and hurling them into open trucks. They were working their way up the street – closing in on her fast. She turned away, rapidly folding down the lapel of her jacket to conceal the star. She ran into the garden of the nearest house. She then passed the row of terraced houses via the garden fences, hurling herself over them or squeezing through gaps in the bushes. Minutes later she came to the end of the row, emerging cautiously, shaking uncontrollably, panting heavily. Her stockings were ripped to shreds and her hands bleeding from the thorns she had scraped through. The coast was clear. The street ahead was quiet. On this occasion she had escaped.

But Edmund had not. At the end of July he received the fateful notice ordering him to report to Amsterdam Central Station, from where he too would be transported to Westerbork.

The notice spelt disaster for Cilla. Having seen what was going on in the streets of her home town she knew things could only be a lot worse away from home. Her instincts told her that if her husband went on that train to Westerbork she would never ever see him again.

Cilla knew from her friend Paula, whose husband Michael worked for the Jewish Council, that a "Sperr" or exemption could be granted selectively for people with connections or for those working in certain industries. Although Michael, as a Jewish Council employee, had been given an exemption together with his wife, he did not have the authority to issue them.

The Nazis gave the Jewish Council hierarchy the authority to issue a certain amount of exemptions. It was a clever strategy of empowering them and making them feel safer than the other Jews. Above all it encouraged continued co-operation between them and the Nazi regime.

But the Biermans had no connections with the hierarchy. So who could Cilla call on for help? Suddenly, she had an idea. She had nothing to lose – it was her only hope.

Heinz Bork was a successful furrier in his forties with whom Edmund had done business on many occasions. Their working relationship had led to a warm friendship over the years. Bork, a third-generation Dutchman with strong ties in Amsterdam, had forged good connections with the local council and business community. Cilla had met him on several occasions and had even hosted him and his wife for a Friday night dinner before the war. He was a man of influence and at this moment her only hope.

Since Cilla had been caught in the deadly raid a few weeks

earlier she barely went out at all now. Having to wear the yellow star was frightening, humiliating and had become very dangerous. But this mission was a matter of life and death.

Courageously, she insisted on going out and told Edmund to watch the children. The couple never went out together anymore. If both were caught, arrested, deported – who would care for the children?

Hurrying through the streets of Amsterdam, the yellow star pinned to her coat, she looked a pitiful sight.

Heinz Bork's fur business was situated over ten blocks away. First she passed the Artis Zoo, that favourite haunt many moons ago but now forbidden to her after more than a hundred years in existence. She looked up and noticed the eagles adorning the gates. She had passed them many times without thinking twice about them. Now she suddenly realised that the Nazi insignia also contained eagles. How fitting they should both have the same Nazi insignia. Let them have each other, she thought in disgust. She moved on faster.

Then she reached the Royal Concertgebouw. It was where Edmund had surprised her on her twenty-second birthday, just after they were married, to hear her favourite violin concerto, No 2 in E minor by Mendelssohn. Since then she had attended as many concerts as she could to enjoy her other favourite composers: Mozart, Tchaikovski and Beethoven. She ran breathlessly past the width of the building, hating its beautiful classical facade. Not only were public places forbidden but some were proactively used as venues to stir up more hatred against her people.

Recently, she had heard that Arthur Seyss-Inquart, the Austrian Reich Commissioner for the German occupied Netherlands had given a speech in this very concert hall. He had said: "We do not consider the Jews to be members of the Dutch nation. The Jews for us are not Dutch ... We will hit the Jews where we can. And those who help them will be hit just as hard." She remembered his words and shuddered.

Minutes later she arrived at the Bork Fur Company, headquartered in a magnificent five storey neo-classical townhouse. The entrance, with its white marble floor and walls, was a picture of grandeur. It had welcomed many upper class women customers in its heyday. In a locked room to the right of the entrance hall was a showroom. Through the window a rail packed with the most luxurious fur coats could be seen – furs of silver and dyed fox, mink dyed muskrat, Asiatic mink, beaver and raccoon. Once upon a time the fur business was booming and the showroom was filled with glamorous ladies trying on the latest furs. These days only a trickle of rich ladies came by to purchase one at heavily reduced prices. It was the summer, there was a war on and money was tight. Fur was a luxury few cared about when food was scarce.

Cilla ran up the stairs, two at a time, to the boss's office on the fourth floor. She knocked loudly and entered without waiting for a response.

"What's the matter?" demanded Mr Bork in alarm as he rose from his desk. He was shocked by the shaking, sweating, ghost-like figure in front of him. It took several minutes before he recognised this trembling, vulnerable woman as Cilla. She was so different from the well-dressed, pretty, smiling young woman he knew.

Cilla gasped out her story in painful, broken words.

Mr Bork sat down, stunned. He knew the situation for the Jews was terrible but now it had come shockingly close to home. He was very fond of the Bierman family. He had always found Cilla elegant, charming and kind and marvelled at how tenderly she looked after her precious children.

"How terrible ... " were all the words he could muster.

He took out his handkerchief and wiped his eyes. This news was devastating. What could he do, he asked? Cilla told him that she had heard that anyone with an exemption could be released. These exemptions were given to people in certain industries such as fur and diamonds or because of special connections. It meant they would be removed from a deportation list ... albeit temporarily.

"I will speak to my contacts immediately. Maybe they can help us."

Cilla was touched by the word "us". Their problem had become his and she was sure he would move heaven and earth to try to help them. Her eyes were dim with tears. It was too much.

Mr Bork got up and moved round the table so he could face her. He was a tall, well built man and next to him Cilla looked tiny. He spoke gently. "I am so sorry for all you are going through. Who would have thought life would turn out like this, and here in Amsterdam? Your family is in my prayers. I promise I will do my best."

Cilla thanked him brokenly and departed.

And true to his word he did his best. The next day the miracle happened. Mr Bork personally came to their home in the morning to deliver his exemption. He had managed to convince the Nazi authorities that Edmund's contribution to the fur industry was invaluable to the war effort. They in turn informed the Jewish Council to take Edmund's name off the list. The paper said he was exempted "bis auf weiteres" – until further notice.

"An exemption," she kept repeating with nervous gratitude. An exemption from what? Terror, oppression, death. "Until further notice," – the words rang through her head. It was a warning to get out fast.

The exemption was probably their luckiest moment and marked a turning point in their lives. They had missed the opportunity to escape to England to join Edmund's brother, and all other borders were now closed. They had taken risks for as long as they could and now there was no hiding the brutal fact that living a minute longer in Amsterdam could be fatal for the entire family. There were no more options left. Just one small chance of survival. This was to escape into hiding. To submerge – immediately.

And so Edmund and Cilla, in whispered conversations, in their bedroom that night, planned their escape. The safest option was to find three hiding places – one for Renata, one for Anton and one for Edmund and Cilla. Through Heinz's connections Edmund made contact with the Resistance and pleaded with them to help his family escape into hiding.

A few weeks later the couple received the news that Renata's hiding place was arranged. Within a few months the children's bedroom at 24 Plantage Parklaan was empty.

They would never return.

CHAPTER TWELVE

Friday 11 September 1942

The Jewish New Year – *Rosh Hashana* – fell on Friday night 11 September. Cilla set the table mechanically in honour of the special festival. There was the symbolic fish head – to represent the head of a year, and sliced apple with honey – to represent a sweet year.

Once she had taken great pride in the details. Not so, this year. There was nothing sweet about her life these days. Her family, including her father and step-mother, took their places at the table. A time usually associated with celebration and family reunion turned into a dinner of panic and fear as the family quietly contemplated their grim future. The strained faces of the adults spoke volumes. In less than a week Renata was to be sent in hiding. Anton would follow soon after.

The following day there were many empty seats in the small unmarked synagogue. People had been arrested, disappeared or simply were too scared to move around. Following the constant raids nowhere was safe, least of all, the prominent synagogue the Biermans used to attend. Instead, Cilla and Edmund went to this much smaller place of worship. The children were safe, guarded at home by their trusted neighbour Ingrid.

There in front of her Cilla recognised the woman who had been wailing in the shop, the year earlier. Then she looked like a middle-aged mother, today she was an old woman. Her eyes were sunken, her then grey hair, now white as it hung loose under her scarf. As the people prayed the woman could be heard crying bitterly. She had been right. Her two sons, her only children, were murdered in Mathausen concentration camp. The widow was now totally alone in this frightening world. Her muffled sounds unnerved Cilla. This woman's fate was exposed. Cilla's was just starting. Very soon she would be separated from her children. What would happen to them?

Cilla tried to concentrate on the prayer book text. She looked down at the words. "Is Ephraim not a treasured son to Me, My child of delights? ... Therefore My heart yearns for him. I will surely have mercy upon him, says the Lord."

Her eyes welled up with tears as she whispered to herself: "My treasured children, my children of delights. My heart yearns for you."

Their separation was imminent. How would she survive? But, more importantly, how would they survive? Would they survive?

CHAPTER THIRTEEN

Friday 25 September 1942

Cilla's thirtieth birthday on Wednesday 23 September would be etched into her memory forever. It was the day she gave her son away, less than a week after she handed over her daughter.

And now two days later life had to continue. Cilla's hand was shaking as she lit the Sabbath candles. As she lit the third and fourth candles, representing her children, she burst into tears again. She was exhausted from the crying. She was inconsolable.

She went into her children's bedroom. Their beds were empty. Her children were gone. They were both really gone. It was final. When would she see them? Would she ever see them? She returned to the living room and stared into the candles' flames.

Two days earlier Cilla had taken five-year-old Anton to Wertheim Park as well. In some ways preparing for his departure was even more difficult. He was old enough to know what was going on and the sadness could be seen in his eyes well before he had to leave his parents.

The night before his departure the three of them ate supper in the kitchen. Cilla had broken the news to him that morning. She explained that it was too dangerous for all of them to go into hiding together and he would be looked after by another family.

"But, mummy who am I going to live with?"

"Darling, you will be looked after by a decent family."

"Will you come and visit me?"

Cilla looked at Edmund. He responded: "We are going to try our very best. There is a war on so we have to see if it is possible."

The parents knew that the likelihood of visiting their son was virtually impossible but at this point they needed to give him a glimmer of hope.

"But mummy, what if I don't like it? What if they don't like me?"

Cilla looked at her plate for a moment and then faced her son and took his hand, "Darling, just be a little patient. At first it will seem a bit difficult but afterwards I am sure it will be okay. You are a big brave boy and we are so very proud of you. Please God we will all see each other soon."

Anton stared at his mother. His face crumpled and he burst into tears again. It was the third time he had cried that day.

"I just don't want to leave you. Never ever. It's not fair. It's just not fair!"

Cilla turned to Edmund. He took off his glasses and dabbed his eyes.

After dinner Grandpa Chaim came over to say goodbye to his first and only grandson. He had watched him grow up since he was born. He had cared for him, nurtured him and loved him deeply. The emotional pain cut so deep. How much worse so was it for his daughter?

Cilla held her little boy's hand all the way down Plantage Parklaan. They were both weeping but they kept their faces down so as not to attract any attention. The contact was the same Resistance man Otto who Cilla had met a few days earlier. When they arrived at the park Cilla approached him. Her watery eyes met his. With his black hair, he could just about pass as Anton's father. Otto looked sorrowfully at the mother and son. He was witnessing her giving away her second child in a matter of days.

The meeting was quick. Mother and son exchanged a tight hug. She then bent down to his level. She wiped his eyes and kissed him.

"Remember, don't forget to say the *Shema* bedtime prayer to yourself every night. Keep it in your heart no matter what you do," she urged, "and when you do, think of me, daddy and Renata and know that we are thinking of you. I love you my sweet prince. I am so proud of you."

Then Otto took Anton's hand affectionately. It was time to go. Quickly, before they aroused suspicion. Cilla was left bereft.

Cilla thought about that painful departure again. How much more could she take? The Sabbath candle lights flickered. She prayed again for her children that were no longer with her.

CHAPTER FOURTEEN

November 1942

illa was devastated. With no children to look after and nowhere for her to go she had plenty of time to think – and to cry. For forty days and forty nights she had been without both children. She could not bear to think how they were managing. She could not help thinking that they had to be suffering immensely without their parents. The only consolation was that Edmund was still there with her. She did not take for granted the fact that he would now have been in Westerbork had he not been exempted – and then her life would have been completely intolerable.

The mission now was to find one more hiding place – for her, her husband, father and step-mother. Finding a place for four adults was a challenge but Cilla insisted that she could not be separated from her father and step-mother. She hoped to hear news from the Resistance about a hiding place imminently.

The terrible situation for the Jews was spiralling out of control – and no one could stem the flow. There was no more talk about being sent to work in Labour Camps or about "relocating" Jews. Instead there were constant rumours about families being deported to the East – to be killed.

In the latest development, the Schouwburg Theatre, around the corner from the Bierman home, had recently turned into a base to round up Jews. The Nazis had ordered that the centrally-located building on the busy Amsterdam boulevard should be used to amass the Jews before deportation. Outside the beautiful building two Nazi soldiers stood guard ensuring no-one inside escaped.

Paula's husband Michael, who worked for the Jewish Council, had now been transferred to a make-shift office in the Theatre. Paula came over to visit Cilla one afternoon. She frequently came to check on her friend, to see how she was coping since handing over her children. Cilla was sitting limply on Anton's empty bed in the lonely apartment. Her face was white, her eyes red, her mood sombre. The two friends hugged each other tight but there was no socialising. Paula had come to bring important information.

"Cilla, you must go into hiding immediately," she blurted out. "Jews don't stand a chance. I have seen things that … oh, it's too terrible."

"What now?" said Cilla. She was past being alarmed. Her only reaction was weary sadness.

"Yesterday I had to deliver documents to Michael at the Theatre. I still can't believe what I saw there," she paused and inhaled deeply. Cilla looked up to meet Paula's eyes.

"You remember the auditorium with the rows of seats and lights, where we used to sit to watch the shows – all gone …

gone. I saw it all from the corridor outside. I saw everything!"
She stopped to compose herself and continued, "the seats have all
been ripped out and now instead there are hundreds and hundreds
of people ... Jewish people ... our friends, our neighbours, our
colleagues, their children and their babies ... all crushed, herded
together ... starving, thirsty, crying, coughing, hysterical ... And
suitcases were piled on the stage, family names painted on them in
great white letters. Ropes were swinging from the ceiling ... like
a hangman's noose. The emergency bulbs were glowing with red
lights, like, like ... blood. It was sickening."

Cilla's eyes filled with tears but she said nothing. Her young
friend continued, choked with emotion.

"Then I saw ... Dora. My friend who moved from Germany to
Amsterdam with me at the same time. Remember her?"

Cilla nodded. Yes of course she remembered. She had met this
pretty, vivacious, young woman at Paula's home a few years ago.

Paula started to cry, "Dora was sitting on the floor, by the
entrance of the auditorium. She was nursing her baby daughter
... except she had nothing to give her. Her baby was screaming.
Dora was hysterical. I couldn't even help. Michael had told me
not to go in the auditorium and not to speak to anyone. He said
it's too dangerous. So she and I just looked at each other. I could
not even talk to her or hug her. It was awful."

Paula was crying hysterically now. Cilla embraced her tightly.
They sat silently for a long minute.

Paula wiped her eyes and looked up, "Cilla, the smell was
horrific. It was foul, stagnant, hellish, you know what I mean? ...
If this is how they treat us in our home city what is deportation
like?"

Cilla was stunned. It was too much to take in.

"First they told us they were relocating the Jews, then they said they were sending us to labour camps. But they were lying, I knew they were lying," whispered Cilla.

"Yes, and Michael has told me what is going on. He said he has seen guards violently dragging men, women and children out of the building and throwing them on to trams ... Throwing little children onto trams," she wailed, as if unable to believe what she was saying herself.

CHAPTER FIFTEEN

In Hiding
1943

I n September 1943, Cilla celebrated the Jewish New Year in an ice-cold basement in Amsterdam. She felt like a rat, lurking underground, scavenging. At least rats could roam freely. She couldn't. She could think of nothing but food, of warmth, and with her yearning for something good to eat came the sharp stabbing anxiety about her children.

This was her seventh hiding place in over nine months. She and Edmund were the *onderduikers* – those who had "dived under". Since December 1942 they had been on the run, guilty of the crime of being Jewish. They had hidden for nights in pasture, hay stacks, coal bins and street carts and lived for days and weeks in attics, basements and "crawl spaces".

After her children had been sent away in September 1942 and Paula had delivered her prophetic warning there was no time to lose. Eventually the Resistance informed them that a place had been found for Edmund, Cilla and her father and step-mother and they would need to move out the next day. They provided them with new identity cards – without the perilous letter J. To the outside world Cilla and Edmund were now Carol and Daniel Ruter. Her father and step-mother were now George and Lisa Merk. Strange names.

Cilla packed all the clothes that could fit in a small suitcase. She squeezed in the keepsakes, the small priceless items – a family photo, the children's hairbrush, a drawing her son had made, a picture of herself and little Renata at ten months-old and the teddy bear Renata had dropped in the park. And her Jewish prayer book.

Her sole luxury was the mink fur stole on her back. Edmund insisted it would keep her warm and in the worst case could be used as a bargaining chip. As soon as he knew he was going into hiding he hurriedly prepared his affairs. He traded his few fur skins for cash and small uncut diamonds. He sewed the diamonds into his jacket pocket and divided the cash between other clothes.

Edmund had savings, a large proportion of which he gave to the Resistance to secure their safety. But there was no knowing how long the war would go on and how much money would be needed.

Jan Menton, a twenty-two-year-old chemistry student at the University of Amsterdam, had dropped out of university to join the Resistance. He belonged to a different underground movement to that of the people who had rescued the children. The tall, sturdy young man was the Biermans' first point of contact when they went into hiding.

When there was a shortage of homes the rescuers resorted to emergency addresses. They could not always trust their own family members but where they could, they often convinced parents or brothers and sisters to help hide people even if just temporarily. Jan's mother Lisbet, an elderly widow, agreed to help hide people in the basement of the modest home in Amsterdam that she shared with Jan, her youngest child.

On the 1 December 1942 Cilla, her husband, father and stepmother arrived late at night at their first hiding place. They were amazed to find four elderly Jewish adults – Frank and Sarah Anders and Abe and Lola Lerman – already in hiding there. The newly enlarged group of eight was squeezed under the floorboards, crammed like sardines, in darkness. They accessed the gloomy space by squeezing through a hole in the floor in the kitchen larder and then jumping on to a big crate that acted as a step.

They crouched around the tiny, dark space silently. During the day they sat carefully on the underfloor pipes and at night slept on thin mattresses. Food and water was passed to them twice daily. Toilet breaks were allowed first thing in the morning and last thing at night. The group silently climbed the large crate and squeezed back through the hole to street level. With the help of Lisbet or Jan standing in the kitchen they were pulled up one by one. They then stood outside the small toilet and relieved themselves one after the other. The chain could not be flushed until the eighth person had finished. The stench was overpowering but there was no option. The toilet could only be flushed at limited times so as not to alert the neighbours. It was the toilet breaks that became the highlights of their day as they could finally stretch their legs, relieve themselves and enjoy some natural daylight.

In the evenings they waited patiently in line to wash themselves in the tiny bathroom on the landing. Just two minutes per person with a pea-size dot of shampoo. Jan had calculated that this was all the time – and water – that could be spared. Too much water passing through the outer pipes over too long a period of time would arouse suspicion on either side of the house. After washing themselves the group returned to their cold, dark, damp hiding place below.

The new life sent shockwaves through Cilla. She thought she would go out of her mind. Even talk had to be kept to the minimum as there could not be too much noise. The darkness and lack of activity led her to have bleak thoughts. She worried endlessly about her children during the day and had strange, painful dreams about them at night, often waking up in a cold sweat. Her daughter's words always came back to haunt her, again and again: "Don't go! Stay, mama. Stay mama, mama ma ... ma, ma ... ma!"

After a couple of days Cilla asked Jan to provide her with one essential item – a note book. She needed a sense of personal control in this black world into which she had been thrown. She noted the date every morning in the diary. It would remind her of the weekly Sabbaths, other festivals and her children's birthdays. The Nazis might have taken away her dignity and freedom but they could not take away her spirituality and values. They had denied her the right to physically observe the Jewish customs but they could not take away her right to cherish them in her heart.

Even in this bleak existence she remained true to the Jewish faith she had loved and embraced all her life. She did not question God for the life she was leading. She accepted it not as the will of God but rather as the evil of humans. On the contrary she prayed to God to keep her family alive.

On day twenty the silent monotony was broken by violent knocking on the door in the early hours of the morning. The Nazi soldiers had showed up to conduct a house search. They were looking for anyone hiding Jews.

"Open up now," they screamed.

Seconds later the thud of heavy hobnailed boots and the howl of dogs barking loudly could be heard inches above their heads as the Nazis conducted their ruthless house search.

The elderly man Frank could not bear the tension and started to weep. Cilla squeezed her father and husband's hands. Sweat poured off her body. The other elderly man Abe urged Frank in a desperate whisper, "If you don't stop that right now, you will get us all killed."

Frank's weeping became louder. Cilla's heart was pounding painfully as she heard doors banging a few feet upstairs. Abe crawled to Frank and put his hands around his neck.

"If you don't stop now, you leave me no choice but to kill you before you get us all killed," he hissed.

Frank's wife Sarah, also in tears, hugged and caressed her husband, calming him down. After a few muffled cries silence resumed. Heavy, raucous breathing was all that could be heard. They had survived the raid. The emotional scars could not be shed so lightly.

This was the third raid on Lisbet Menton's home in a month. She was not sure if it was bad luck or because the Nazis suspected her home of being a hide-out. Either way, the small elderly woman couldn't handle the pressure any longer. Moreover, she was at risk of exposing the hidden Jews because of her nerves.

They would have to leave before another search was carried out, possibly the following morning. They were forced to leave that very evening, very late at night when the streets were quiet.

As the war showed no sign of ending the rescuers found it increasingly difficult to find homes quickly. Finding a place for four adults together, immediately, now proved impossible. Even more dangerous, travelling together as a group of four looked too conspicuous. Jan broke the news to Cilla, telling her that she and her father would have to go their separate ways from now on. Having always felt responsible for her father since her mother died, Cilla was stunned. It was another brutal blow.

She spent the remaining hours in Lisbet's basement close to her father. They talked, laughed and cried. Saying goodbye to her father was one of the most difficult tasks of her life. How could she find the words? For her father it was as if a limb were being cut off. Life without his lovely, smiling, precious Cilla was not life. It was simply survival.

Father and daughter prayed that they would see each other again soon – but in their hearts they knew with the heaviness of despair that this could so easily be the end. A single kiss goodbye and Cilla was gone.

At 2 a.m. that night Cilla and Edmund left Lisbet Menton's home with nowhere to go. Jan could not arrange sleeping arrangements for all eight of them at such short notice. In fact he had found places for three couples but not a fourth. As Edmund and Cilla were the youngest it meant that they would be homeless for the night. Jan told them to reconnect with him at 5 p.m. the following day at the park around the corner from his mother's home.

Cilla and Edmund found themselves alone and abandoned for

the night. They wandered the dark, deserted streets with their meagre possessions. The suitcases had been discarded as they were dangerous give away signs. Their possessions were now reduced to a bag each.

That night they wandered the streets like homeless strays. Finally they found an abandoned food cart. They squeezed in and stayed there until dawn, huddled beneath a damp rubber cover. Stiff and aching, they emerged at the crack of dawn filled with renewed fear. It was 6 a.m., Tuesday 22 December. For the next ten hours they wandered the streets. Although they had new identities they felt they physically looked like fugitives. The tell tale signs were all there – exhaustion, crumpled clothes and above all fear. That could be spotted a mile off. They walked from park bench to park bench, criss-crossing the city and hoping to avoid Nazi soldiers, Nazi patrols and Nazi sympathisers.

At last at 5 p.m. they met Jan at the park. He warned them to keep their distance as they followed him to the train station. If the Biermans were arrested then at least Jan would not be caught as well. He bought the train tickets and motioned them to follow him onto the train that was just about to leave. There they sat opposite him like strangers. The train started. Suddenly, through the partition into the next carriage they heard the sound of raucous, rowdy voices. Germans! Jan hurriedly instructed them with hand movements to sit separately. Cilla understood immediately and moved three seats away from her husband. She picked up a newspaper from the floor and looked over it, apparently absorbed. Her heart was pounding and her hands shook violently. It would be a tragedy to be arrested because of shaking hands, she thought.

The hours of hiding in the cart and walking the streets of

Amsterdam had made Edmund look like a tramp. He pulled his cap over his face and stared at the floor. The moments dragged by slowly. The Nazi officers strutted through their carriage confidently. They were joyful, upbeat and ... very drunk.

"Oh no" Cilla thought. She had heard the stories of drunken soldiers kicking and taunting Jews on the streets. It was a game to see which soldier could cause more pain and suffering to their victims. "Now it's our turn," she thought. Her heart was still thumping painfully. She stared at the words unblinking, uncomprehending. The soldiers' boots echoed in the background till she could no longer hear them.

It seemed that they were not looking to arrest any Jews that moment. Cilla breathed a huge sigh of relief. Edmund was about to move next to her but Cilla motioned him to stay exactly where he was. No need to attract any attention from the other passengers. There was no knowing who could be trusted.

They arrived at Haarlem. Outside the station they followed Jan at a safe distance. His pace was fast and urgent. Twenty-five minutes later they arrived at a small office building. At the top of two flights of stairs they reached a locked door. Jan unlocked the door and led the couple into a small room in which there were filing cabinets, two armchairs and a coffee table. It was the waiting room of a doctor's surgery. Hiding places came in all shapes and sizes. The doctor, a friend of Jan's, was away for the Christmas holidays and they could stay there until his return in January. Jan left them with bread, water and tinned food. He showed them where the public toilets were that served all the offices in the building. They could use them outside office hours – before 8 a.m. and after 7 p.m. – but never in between.

For the next few days they lived in terror and boredom in the doctor's surgery, living on scanty rations and reading out of date newspapers.

On Christmas Day their restrictions were eased slightly as all the offices were closed. It was a Friday and early evening was the eve of the Sabbath. Without any candles, Cilla turned to the box of matches in Edmund's pocket. She struck two matches, held them up and recited the Sabbath prayer – the last for 1942.

CHAPTER SIXTEEN

1943

On Monday 4 January 1943 the Biermans were forced out of their latest hiding place as the doctor's surgery re-opened. They spent another forlorn evening wandering the unfamiliar streets of Haarlem until they found their next hide-out. Edmund spotted an abandoned warehouse that could be accessed through a broken window. The floors were littered with broken glass and it was freezing. But it had a roof and would keep them safe and dry. As planned, Jan met them the next day at the train station, where he took them on foot to their next hiding place – the home of Mr and Mrs Van de Kieps.

Tom and Maria Van de Kieps had five young children, none of whom were allowed to know about the hidden Jewish couple for fear they would blurt out the secret at school. Cilla and Edmund lived in their attic without heating or lighting. There was nothing in the room but one narrow bed. They lay there most of the day, pale and shivering, only allowed out when the children were out the house. Thankfully a pack of playing cards broke the maddening monotony. The attic window looked out into the street. Often Cilla would see and hear children playing with their skipping ropes. It was agonising.

February was an especially difficult month for the couple. On the 6 February Cilla marked her diary with a red pen – Renata's second birthday. Two weeks later on the twentieth Cilla marked her diary again to note Anton's sixth birthday. She had been in hiding just a couple of months and her nerves were frayed and jagged. How would she endure the future, whatever it held for her? There had been no word about her children. The silence was torture. Her heart ached.

The three months in Haarlem ended abruptly when Mr and Mrs Van de Kieps said they could no longer cope with the secrecy and strain. When they had originally accepted the Biermans they had hoped the war would be over soon. But it had not and now there was no end in sight. They contacted Jan and said that if a home could be found for the Biermans they would like to be absolved of their responsibility.

So on 4 April 1943 the Biermans were sent to a farm in Lisse owned by the Zwiet family. There they joined Albert and Dina Kohler, also in hiding with their two teenage daughters Lisa and Anna. The six of them lived on mattresses in the adjoining barn. As Gonda, the twenty-year-old daughter of the family, worked in the local Dutch Fascist NSB Party office, the Germans never suspected anything and had never raided the farm. With the NSB badge on her coat, Gonda, a secret Resistance worker, was sometimes beaten up for being a traitor. But at the beginning of June someone tipped off the Nazis and the farm was raided.

Luck was on the Bierman's side as at the exact time of the raid they had ventured out for a toilet break. The Kohler family was caught, arrested and sent to Vught concentration camp, together with Gonda.

The months on the run had reduced Cilla to a ghost of her former self. She could just about cope with the heartache of missing and worrying about her children, the constant sadness, the monotony, the depression, the loneliness. But never the fear – the fear of finally being caught would never leave her.

Devastated, defeated and totally desperate the Biermans were on the move again. Jan told them to make their way to Amsterdam Central Station, where their new contact, Pieter P, was waiting for them under the clock tower. He would be wearing a red and yellow checked scarf.

Two Pieters worked for this group of Resistance workers. They were known as Pieter P and Pieter T. Pieter P was a member of the Calvinist Church. He and his family were shocked and saddened by the fate of the Jews and became involved in helping find hiding places. As expected Pieter P was waiting by the kiosk.

The Biermans walked into the courtyard outside the huge station. Cilla looked up above the building and noticed for the first time the words inscribed in French over the top. *Je Maintiendra* – I will maintain or I will prevail. It was the saddest irony.

Cilla spotted Pieter P. As instructed she went up to him and asked the code question – "Is it ten o'clock?" to which he responded "No, it's ten past."

Ten seconds later he moved away and the couple followed. They were back in the Amsterdam they knew so well. It was a strange feeling, walking to a hiding place in their home town. Suddenly, realizing this, terrible fear gripped Cilla. Every step was fraught with panic – what if they were stopped and caught? Everything about her appearance could be a give-away – dark hair, anxious face, crumpled coat. She knew her whole demeanour was dangerous. Somehow Edmund managed to look calmer. He held her hand and gently pulled her along.

Half an hour later, Cilla could not believe her eyes as she walked down Plantage Parklaan, actually passing the home that the family had been forced to abandon. A vision rose before her eyes: walking back in, reunited with her children, kissing them good night, all safe together under one roof. How had she never appreciated the simple normality of her former life? She walked past the door, haggard and exhausted, gazing at the blue-and-white mosaic tiles that had charmed her into choosing her first family home. Edmund put his arm around her.

"Come on Cilenku," he whispered affectionately. They walked on with a sense of urgency.

Ten minutes later Pieter P stopped abruptly ahead of them. He looked around cautiously and took a few more steps up to the door of a pretty, neat, narrow house. He knocked. The door opened. He motioned the Biermans to hurry inside. Their new hiding place was on Plantage Kerklaan, just a short walk from their former home. It was their seventh hide-out.

Cilla made her way down to the cellar mechanically, exhausted. But the sight that confronted her galvanised her. There, sitting on the floor were six children aged roughly between four and eight years old. She covered her mouth. Tears sprang to her eyes as the solemn faces stared back at her.

She approached the forlorn group. She sat beside them and spoke to the oldest looking boy.

"What is your name?"

"Anton," he whispered.

Her heart skipped a beat.

"How long have you been here?"

"Just a few days"

Is this what abandoned children look like? She thought of her own two and wondered for the thousandth time where they were and how they were coping.

These children had come from the child care-centre across the road from the Schouwburg Theatre, where their parents had been held before being deported to concentration camps. They were the lucky ones – those who had been smuggled out thanks to the bravery of a few people. Walter Süskind, manager of the Schouwburg, headmistress Henriëtte Pimentel and Resistance worker Joop Woortman together with others organised the dangerous and complex rescue of hundreds of children from the childcare centre.

Little children were smuggled out in rucksacks, laundry baskets and baby carriages, while the older ones were sometimes able to escape when a tram passed by, blocking the view of the guard outside the Schouwburg. Hundreds were smuggled out through the back garden and into the adjacent Protestant teacher training college with the support and co-operation of its director Johan Van Hulst. They would later be picked up by the Resistance.

Cilla's heart was heavy at the sight of these abandoned children who she imagined would probably never see their parents again. She spent the rest of her time in the basement devoted to their welfare. Apart from eight-year-old Anton, there was seven-year-old Abram, six-year-old twins Eliza and

David, five-year-old Silvia and little Felix who was just four years old and had a shock of blonde hair and dazzling blue eyes.

Cilla devoted her energies to the poor children. She hugged them, caressed them, sang with them and cried with them. She requested a few children's books from Pieter P, which he dutifully brought her. Every night she read to the children the stories she should have been telling her own children. She also produced Renata's precious teddy bear, the one her little daughter had dropped the day she was taken away. It was a small source of comfort for Cilla, who often hugged it. Now she shared this precious teddy with these children, hoping they too could get some comfort from it.

She could not give them any optimistic news but she could at least try to make them feel better. She hoped her affection would give them the strength to carry on.

It was without doubt the lowest point of Cilla's life. In her diary for the date 4 June 1943 she just wrote: "In hiding with the poor Schouwburg children."

Edmund and Cilla spent almost four months in the basement, the sole adults with the children. The days were getting longer. The building they lived in appeared to be a former family home that was now converted into the headquarters of an organisation. The details were sketchy and Cilla and Edmund knew not to ask more than they were told. Movement was restricted to going upstairs just for toilet breaks.

One day in August they were delighted to learn that they could go outside, as the building was totally empty. Pieter P led them to a tiny patio adjacent to the kitchen. There they breathed in the summer air and blinked in the unaccustomed glare of the sunlight.

This indulgence was repeated a few more times that month. Cilla, Edmund and the children breathed in the air, intoxicated by the sweet, fresh scent. By September life resumed to its normal state of depression, desolation and darkness.

Cilla found out from Pieter P the exact date of the Jewish New Year, as it changed from year to year. She wondered if he could obtain some provisions for her. It was more important than ever that the children celebrated the festival: she hoped it would give them a shred of hope and joy.

On Wednesday evening 29 September the six children and two adults clustered together on the stone floor of the basement around wooden crates that served as a table. Pieter had been able to obtain the few items on Cilla's list. There sat the fish head, the chopped apples, a small loaf of bread and a tiny bowl of honey. Shivering, Cilla sat at the head of the makeshift table next to Edmund. The children, draped in blankets, dipped the apple in the honey. The sweet, sticky honey finally brought a wan smile to their faces. A ray of sunshine into the darkness.

CHAPTER SEVENTEEN

November 1943 – May 1944

Cilla had become so absorbed with the children under her watch that when she discovered that a better hiding place had been found for her and Edmund, she felt a stab of alarm. Pieter assured her that a more suitable home was being sought for the children too. This dark basement was too grim, he conceded, and when better places became available they had to be grabbed immediately.

On their last day together, Cilla hugged the children tightly. Over the last few months they had grown as close as mother and children ever could. Their desolate faces, the despair in their eyes, was hard to bear.

On a bitingly cold, starless winter night Cilla and Edmund met Pieter on the street corner. They followed him to a canal, where they were herded quickly onto a boat manned by a rugged, white-bearded old man. The skipper said nothing as he steered the nervous couple on what seemed like an endless journey through the cold night wind. Eventually they arrived at their destination – Hoorn.

There they were met by another underground worker, Pieter T, the key contact for that region. Pieter T was the oldest Resistance worker they had come across so far. The thirty-nine-year-old, stockily built man did not look like the typical heroic rescuer. But although he was already approaching middle age, he was dedicated to his work and had many extraordinary talents. A skilled artist, he could expertly forge a document that was as good as the original. And thanks to his resilience and sheer energy, he had become a dynamic and indispensible force in the underground movement. The couple followed Pieter T for twenty minutes until they arrived at their destination – an elegant townhouse in a leafy street – belonging to Hans and Ella Bok.

Hans opened the door, warmly greeting the Biermans as if they were old friends. This was partly strategy so that no passer-by would suspect anything but mostly because, together with his wife, they genuinely and warmly welcomed those they were hiding.

Hans and Ella Bok were extraordinary people. Since the summer of 1942 the Catholic couple proactively looked to help the Jews. Hans had been a successful businessman, with a large shoe factory in the north of Holland. He sold the company before the war so that he could retire and travel with his wife. When the war broke out he felt that God had given him his free time and wealth to put to better use. Doing nothing, they said, was "like collaborating with murderers." They believed they had a duty to protect and shelter as many Jews as they could.

The couple refused to be paid for their efforts and, on the contrary, contributed generously to the Resistance fund. Their three children were grown up and had left home. Their two elder daughters were married and their youngest son was working away from home. They had not even disclosed their plans to their children. Although they trusted them implicitly, it would be putting their children and their sons-in-law in danger to share their secret with them. It was too great a risk to take.

Hans and Ella had taken to their role as rescuers with great fervour. At first they had started with one couple and then, as the months passed, they added to the group until there were ten people in the house. Hans told Ella that they had reached capacity and could not accept any more Jews. Ella begged Hans to squeeze in just one more couple. It was another one of Cilla and Edmund's lucky moments.

Cilla and Edmund entered the hallway of the elegant house. They felt both gratitude and shame for being such a burden on these kind people. Blonde-haired Ella appeared, a beaming smile on her face. She welcomed them warmly, took their bags and led them into the kitchen. On the table stood a vase of red tulips, a sponge cake and a pot of tea. It was so different from the chill, the hunger and the cold of the basement they had just left. Cilla was confused. In the other hiding places there had been so much fear and surreptitiousness yet here she suddenly felt as if she were visiting a friend.

"Let me take your coats. You must be exhausted and starving, please please sit down," exclaimed their hostess. They sat down wearily while Ella poured tea. The tea and cake were delicious, tasty memories of an almost forgotten, blissful past.

Ella welcomed all those she was protecting with a home-made cake. Although the ingredients were scarce she believed it was an important gesture. She wanted to make those she called her "guests" as comfortable as possible: a cake gave them a feeling of being a bit special, rather than a huge burden.

Although there were four unused bedrooms in their home the Boks had been advised to hide everyone in their attic – one hiding place was safer in the event of a raid. The attic was a large space that had been used as storage by the family. It was concealed in the ceiling of the second floor and could be accessed by a ladder that popped out when the attic trapdoor was pushed open by a long stick.

In the last few months the Boks had worked tirelessly to make the attic more comfortable. They sectioned off an area to serve as a changing room, laid down old carpets, hung curtains on the small attic windows, and brought in a table, chairs and many books.

Ella led Cilla and Edmund up the ladder to the attic. There they were confronted with a sea of mattresses and a crowd of people. Cilla gazed in amazement. She immediately noticed the windows – the luxury of daylight! Then she turned to the group before her – old, young and middle aged people sitting on their mattresses. She noticed a striking, blonde young woman who was clearly pregnant. Her stare was interrupted by Ella's beaming voice.

"Hello, everyone. Here are Cilla and Edmund from Amsterdam. They are joining us. Please can we go around the room introducing ourselves."

It felt so surreal.

And so life began in their new hiding place. Finally, it was something like "life" compared to their previous "existence". After being cooped up in so many cramped, tiny spaces, the Boks' attic was an unbelievable luxury. Everything Cilla had taken for granted in her old life before she went into hiding – light, air, washing her face, stretching her legs, using the toilet when she needed and not speaking in hushed tones – was now a luxury.

The raids were rare in this area so, as long as they did not stand near windows and were generally cautious, they were allowed considerable movement within the house. This meant that their showers could last longer than two minutes and they could relieve themselves when they wanted, rather than just at morning and night. But movement was limited to indoors. The hidden people were not allowed access to the beautiful garden for fear that the Boks' neighbours would spot them.

Every morning Hans opened the attic door and brought down the ladder. His guests came down one by one to use one of the two bathrooms. Then they went downstairs for a basic breakfast of thinly-sliced bread and butter, sliced tomatoes and apples and a pot of weak tea. Although the Resistance had taken a lot of ration cards to help feed the big group in the house, food was still scarce. Practical Hans monitored the food system and saved any leftovers. He also devised a list of duties that needed to be done – cooking, cleaning, laundry – and organised a rota so that a good routine was established. The hidden Jews welcomed the rota. Not only did they want to pull their weight but it broke the monotony and took their minds off their darker fears.

The Boks went out of their way to understand the customs and laws of their Jewish guests. The Biermans, together with an elderly couple – Rachel and Jakob Klein – were the most orthodox members of the group while the others ranged in observance from limited to none.

Ella quizzed Cilla on the many Jewish laws, especially the dietary requirements. From then on she no longer knowingly cooked milk and meat together and tried to buy as many vegetarian products as possible. She also ensured Friday night dinners were prepared well before the Sabbath came in at nightfall, so that no electricity was used during the twenty-five hour period.

That first December Friday night Cilla lit the two candles prepared for her by her kind hostess. Out of her pocket she took her two precious photos – one of Anton as a baby with Edmund's family and one of her holding Renata as a baby. She gazed at them longingly and closed her eyes. She thought of her own children and then of the ones she had left behind in the last hiding place. Tears pricked at her eyelids. Then her thoughts turned to her father and his wife. Where were they? She missed her father so much. She prayed they were still alive.

The sensitivity and care the Boks showed was so uplifting, it somehow made the painful thoughts and dreams more bearable. Cilla was touched by Ella's kindness and forged a warm rapport with the older woman. She enjoyed accompanying Ella in the kitchen, helped with the cooking and even taught her how to bake her famous Kokosh chocolate cake, albeit with much less cocoa. In turn, Ella was moved by this gentle young mother. She pitied her desperately and cared for her as if she were her own daughter. Cilla's sad, tired eyes told their own story.

The anxiety that hung over the house could never disappear. While they all tried to busy themselves talking, reading or playing cards, the sound of someone sobbing frequently punctuated the quiet. Everyone had a tragic story to tell.

Edmund feared for the father and siblings he had left behind in Czechoslovakia. News from the East had reached horrifying proportions as stories emerged of Jews being murdered in wholesale massacres – in "gas chambers" inside "extermination camps". It was impossible to believe such stories … but they haunted Edmund's dreams.

As for his other two brothers, he prayed that Usher was still safe in England with his family following the intense bombing of London in "The Blitz," that had taken place in 1940 and 1941. He also prayed his young brother Shia was surviving the tough army conditions, wherever in the world he was now.

Cilla quickly forged a close bond with the young pregnant woman. Her name was Lilly Frankel and she too was from Amsterdam. The twenty-three-year-old had been married for just a year. Her husband Bernard, a doctor, had been sent to Westerbork in July and she had not heard a word from him since he was deported. He did not even know she was pregnant. Lilly did not know where her parents and younger sister Lara were – or if they were even alive. She was fighting for survival all alone.

Cilla was saddened. The poor girl was due to give birth in just a few weeks. This war made Cilla realise that no matter how bad things were for herself, someone, somewhere close by was suffering even more. Edmund had nearly been sent to Westerbork. How fortunate she was to have him by her side when others were struggling to survive on their own. Cilla wanted to give Lilly emotional strength so that she would no longer feel totally alone.

Lilly was the only person allowed unrestricted access to the bedrooms in the house at night. The elder members of the group occasionally rested in the beds during the day as the mattresses were much more comfortable, but never at night. But as Lilly's pregnancy advanced she needed access to the toilet regularly. The Boks decided that one person sleeping there was a small calculated risk worth taking and so she slept in their eldest daughter Ineke's childhood bedroom.

The Boks kept visits of friends to a bare minimum. When they entertained, which was very rarely, they closed the attic door and warned the group to keep noise to a minimum. Their children's visits were also planned well in advance as they lived far away ... except for the time their eldest daughter Ineke came to visit unexpectedly one day shortly before Christmas. Her parents tried to act naturally. Ella pulled her daughter into the kitchen for a cup of tea and motioned Hans to deal with the situation upstairs. He hurried up, checked no-one was in the bathrooms, climbed the ladder and told the group that he was closing the attic door. With a sigh of relief he went back downstairs.

But Ineke appeared in no rush to leave. She chatted endlessly, enjoying her parents' company. When she needed the toilet she went up to the old bathroom next to her old bedroom. She was startled to encounter a young, heavily pregnant woman leaving as she was about to enter. They froze.

"Hello ... who are you?" was all Lilly could muster.

"Who am I? Who are you?" retorted Ineke.

"Erm ... a friend of the Boks."

"I'm their daughter. I don't know you. Who, may I ask, are you?"

"... Lilly."

"And what are you doing here?"

"Perhaps it's better ... erm ... if you, um, ask your parents."

Lilly was shaking. Ineke went straight back downstairs. Lilly strained her ears to hear what was going on. Was that shouting? She could not be sure but the voices below sounded angry. The secret was out – how would their daughter react? Lilly stood rooted to the spot for what seemed an endless time.

Several minutes later a solemn-looking Ella went upstairs to Lilly. She put her arm around the young woman's shoulders.

"Don't worry, everything is alright. Please come with me to meet our daughter properly."

Ineke was at the kitchen table with her father.

"I am truly sorry for shocking you. I was really shocked to see you," said Ineke apologetically.

"Me too."

"As you can imagine, my parents never told me. And I never told them."

"Told them what?"

"I never told them that my husband and I are also hiding a family. I am so happy it is all out in the open now."

Ineke had been hiding a mother, father and their young son for the past four months. Despite the risk, Ella was so pleased her daughter not only had the moral sense but also had the courage and conviction to act on it. Lilly took a seat in the kitchen and exhaled slowly. The shock had shaken her badly.

By January 1944 a decision needed to be made swiftly about how Lilly was going to have her baby. The Boks thought about sending her to the local hospital. With her forged papers they considered this might be worth the risk. But no, Lilly would have none of it, it was far too risky. Delivering the baby at home seemed the only option. Without a trustworthy doctor to hand Lilly said she would be most happy if old Mrs Klein, a former midwife, would agree to deliver her baby. Rachel Klein needed no convincing. She said it would be an honour.

Lilly's situation haunted Cilla. Instead of only dreaming about Renata, Anton and her father, she started dreaming about Lilly as well. She woke up at nights in a cold sweat. How would Lilly cope? What were the long term prospects for her baby? How could they prevent the baby from crying at times when it might be dangerous for any sound to emerge from their hiding place? And what if they were forced out the house? How would mother and child survive? After a few nights she confided her fears to Ella and suggested a new plan. Lilly, with her blonde hair, did not look Jewish and wouldn't attract suspicion. Why not arrange for her to have new identification papers made up as "Lilly Bok"? Lilly Bok could be her daughter-in-law, married to her son Henri. In that way she could stay in their house indefinitely and the baby's future would be protected. Ella listened intently. Cilla's words made a lot of sense. So Hans made contact with Pieter T. With enough notice, new ID cards could be made up. Lilly would receive her new identity within weeks.

Although the expected birth date was still four weeks away in mid-February, Cilla warned that they should be prepared for an early birth too. Another spare bedroom was promptly prepared to be a delivery room. Ella requested that Pieter T start delivering the medical provisions and a crib in preparation for the home birth.

Meanwhile Edmund received the best gift of his life on his birthday that year. Cilla had pressed Pieter T to see if he could get any word on her children's safety. The complicated network of rescuers from different groups made it hard to access information.

Helga and Otto, who had taken Renata and Anton, formed part of a separate network from that of Pieter T and his colleagues. Nevertheless Pieter T said he would see what he could do.

On 28 January, on Edmund's thirty fourth birthday, Pieter T came to deliver some medical supplies for the impending birth of Lilly's baby. With him he brought long-awaited news, confirming that Renata was safe with her family and that Anton was safe and living with another family. He had heard this news via a colleague who had connections with the other Resistance group. He was not given the names and addresses of the families hiding the children. After almost eighteen months of silence this was the best news ever. The desperate parents hugged each other tightly.

Hugely relieved, Cilla turned her attention back to Lilly. She suggested that she sleep next to the young woman in Ineke's old bedroom until the birth. Edmund was understanding and supportive. Lilly was touched by Cilla's devotion, which helped her through her anxiety and sorrow.

Lilly went into labour two weeks early, in the middle of the night. Rachel Klein was awoken and got to work. Cilla was her assistant. The labour was long and extremely painful. Cilla held Lilly's hand and wiped her brow. Ella was on hand to bring her drinks and encourage her with tender words.

Dawn broke on a beautiful day – the February sun shining into the bedroom. The swallows fluttered in the morning sky, free and graceful. One could be forgiven for thinking that bringing a child into this glorious world was a fine idea.

Rachel delivered the screaming baby girl at midday on Wednesday 2 February 1944. She expertly cut the umbilical cord and handed the baby to an exhausted but elated mother, who held her tightly and wept. She now had part of her husband back.

Lilly had already decided on the name, if it was a girl. She called her daughter "Cella". It was a combination of the names Cilla and Ella – in recognition of the two women who had cared so deeply for her.

When old Jakob Klein heard the name his eyes lit up, "Goodness, do you know what the word Cella means in Hebrew?"

No, she did not.

"It means rock. As in rock of support – which biblical figures used to refer to their praise of God."

Lilly thought how Cilla and Ella had been her rock of support and now how her daughter would be too. It was a truly fitting name.

Cilla continued to sleep next to Lilly after the baby's birth. When baby Cella awoke for feeds during the night Cilla woke up too, took the baby out of her crib and handed her over to her mother. For Cilla it was a welcome distraction. February was a particularly harsh month for her as she thought about Renata turning three and Anton turning seven. It broke her heart to think that she probably would not even be able to recognise her daughter in the street – she would have been transformed from a baby to a little girl.

Baby Cella brought unbelievable joy to the Jews in hiding. She was a breath of fresh air, the first genuinely good news that they had experienced. As the months passed and she grew they held her, hugged her and cooed over her. She was surrounded by love in a world of conflict and hate.

But this joy was short lived. On Thursday 11 May Pieter T came over late at night to inform Hans and Ella that the Nazis had been tipped off about activities in the house. Luckily the Resistance had been tipped off too. At the crack of dawn, the eleven adults were speedily herded out through the back garden, with their few possessions.

After their house guests had left Hans and Ella got to work quickly. They went up to the attic and piled the mattresses in the corners of the large space and covered them with dust sheets. They lugged their empty suitcases back upstairs and threw them into the attic. Finally, in a last minute moment of inspiration, Ella dragged up the vacuum cleaner and blew frantically though its pipe. Out came an enormous cloud of dust, settling over the attic. It now looked as if it has been undisturbed for years.

Exactly thirty minutes later five Nazi soldiers arrived at the house for a search. They banged furiously on the door. Ella opened the door, surprise on her face.

"What is the matter?"

"We are conducting a house search," said the tall SS town commander abruptly. He led the soldiers in.

"I don't understand. What are you looking for?" she asked in an innocent voice.

"Like you don't know? Jews of course."

"We don't have any. But you are welcome to search of course."

"We don't need your permission. Let's go," he barked.

They stampeded through the house, overturning tables and flinging open cupboards. They swept their batons viciously through the Boks' possessions: photo frames crashed to the floor, splinters of glass strewn everywhere, ornaments were flung to the floor and smashed to dust. Ella retreated to the kitchen where Lilly sat nervously with baby Cella and Hans was pacing up and down.

Five minutes later the commander walked into the kitchen. He glanced at Lilly and the baby. He turned to Hans, "You, come upstairs now."

Hans followed obediently. On the landing the commander began hitting the ceiling with his baton. He was searching for a hollow spot concealing a trap door.

"Your attic. Where is the access point?"

"Over here."

"Open it."

Hans slowly approached the airing cupboard to get the stick that opened the door. He hoped he hadn't left any evidence. The clear up had been hasty.

"Hurry up," snarled the commander. "We have other things to do."

Hans clicked the door open with the stick. His heart was pounding. "There it is," said Hans hoping that this would be the end of the search.

"Pull the ladder down."

He shouted at the soldiers to go up. Three soldiers climbed the ladder and entered the attic. They flung the sheets aside and probed and kicked the mattresses and suitcases. They were intent on finding something – or someone.

"Absolutely nothing," came the first soldier's response.

The commander eyed Hans slowly, said nothing and went downstairs. The ordeal was not over. The commander went back into the kitchen. Hans followed him.

"Tell me who this is?" he asked, pointing to Lilly.

"Why, she's my daughter-in-law and this is our beautiful grand-daughter," said Ella.

"Where is the husband?"

"You mean my son," said Ella firmly. "He is helping the war effort. He has not even met his daughter, sadly."

The commander stared at Lilly and then her baby and then back at Lilly for a long moment.

"Please," pleaded Ella, "not so loud. The baby just fell asleep."

"That is not my concern," he pointed to Hans, "we search till we find. Maybe the first time we are not lucky but be sure we get there in the end. And anyone caught helping will meet the same fate as that of the Jews. That would include you, your wife, your daughter-in-law and your very precious grand-daughter."

He paused allowing them to digest his words, "Remember – we search till we find."

He turned on his heel, his soldiers following suit, leaving Hans, Ella and Lilly shaken to the core in a house that had been turned upside down.

CHAPTER EIGHTEEN

May – September 1944

The Boks would never know how their secret had been uncovered but it had and it was now far too dangerous to shelter the group again. There had been no time for goodbyes. The people they had grown to love and appreciate day in, day out for so many months had gone, in a flash. Their best chance of survival so far had been in the Boks' house. Out on the streets they were now in grave danger. The Boks and Lilly were bereft. Baby Cella would prove to be a real rock of comfort for the three grief-stricken adults.

Although most of the South of the Netherlands was liberated in the second half of 1944 – following D-day on 6 June when the allied forces invaded Northern France – the rest of the country was still under occupation. The Biermans were on the run again, entering the most dangerous phase of their ordeal.

Following their hurried escape from the Boks' comfortable home, desperate measures were taken to find another hiding place. Pieter T arranged for them to move to a barge owned by the skipper who had taken them to the Boks' house. Late at night they boarded the run-down rusty barge and were herded into the cabin down below. The skipper's name was Boris. His wife Clara was a short stocky woman with unkempt grey hair. They showed no emotion or care towards the couple in front of them. For them it was purely a business transaction. The skipper needed the money and wanted to be handsomely compensated for the risk he was taking. It was lucky Edmund had traded his diamond stones for cash with Hans Bok. Hans had given him a more than fair price for the two stones. It had come at the right moment as the skipper's price for shielding them was avaricious.

The months in the cramped barge were depressing not only for the sheer discomfort and intense hunger but all the more so because Boris and Clara didn't hide their contempt for the Biermans. They barely talked to Cilla and Edmund and gave them minuscule portions of food while gorging themselves with generous servings in front of them. At night, when the temperature dropped to very low levels, Cilla wore her fur stole. The first time she wore it she noticed Clara eyeing the jacket intensely and felt uncomfortable.

Pieter T came to the barge every few weeks to instruct Boris about one-off jobs for the Resistance. On the most recent visit Edmund had asked Pieter T if they could move to a new hiding place. But hiding places had now become scarce to the point of almost non-existent. Pieter T insisted that the priority was survival. Moreover, Boris and Clara were trustworthy, no matter how unpleasant they were. In this war, where traitors frequently reared their ugly heads, trustworthy people could not be taken for granted.

By the end of August Edmund's cash had shrunk almost to

nothing. He would need to speak to Boris about negotiating a new deal. As it happened, Boris wanted to speak to Edmund too. He approached him one quiet evening as he sat beside Cilla on the splintered, weathered bench. His wife Clara hung close by.

"Mr Bierman. My wife and I have been thinking. We were told that your time here would be temporary. As you can see, the weeks have turned into months. The Occupation is dragging on. To be honest we thought it would soon be over after D-Day but … We don't know how much longer it will be."

"Yes," said Edmund, fearing where this conversation was heading.

"My wife and I took a huge risk in sheltering you. Each day that passes is an increased risk for us, you understand." He paused for effect and continued, "We think that in order to compensate for this risk our payment should be increased – as of next week, starting from 1 September."

There was barely enough money to last on the agreed rate, never mind an increase. But Edmund knew that Boris had the upper hand. He and Cilla were in desperate need of protection and Boris was the only person able to provide it.

"I am sorry. But we are really running out of funds. I have virtually no cash left as it is. We simply can't afford to give any more," he said.

Clara had heard enough. She approached the men, "Excuse me, I have an idea … What about your wife's fur stole? If you cannot pay us with money I am sure we can come to an agreement about the jacket."

"Erm, I see. Let me think about it," said Edmund cautiously. "Let me talk to Cilla and I am sure we can come to an arrangement."

Cilla looked down at the weather beaten wooden floor boards. The conversation made her feel desperately vulnerable. If only they could move away from this mercenary couple.

Their salvation came in a most unexpected way. A few days after this conversation, elderly Lisbet Menton, the mother of Jan the Resistance worker, passed away from a heart attack. The day after the funeral, practical Jan re-opened the basement of her small Amsterdam home to welcome Jews in hiding again.

Pieter T came to deliver the news to Edmund and Cilla. She was sad for Jan. She knew what it was to lose a mother and at such a young age. But she was so relieved that they could finally move. Never in her wildest dreams would she have expected such a dark, damp, depressing basement to be her salvation. Plans were made for them to leave the next day.

Before he left the barge, Cilla asked Pieter T to bring her something very important for her departure – a bottle of peroxide.

The last time she had walked the streets of Amsterdam she had felt so vulnerable and exposed with her black hair and anxious face. She had heard about Jews dyeing their hair blonde to minimise arousing suspicion. She felt the need to do the same. Luckily her ID photo pictured her with a scarf covering her dark hair, otherwise this plan wouldn't make any sense.

Clara and Boris could not hide their frustration that their extra source of income was ending. It was sheer bad luck. Boris had anticipated an endless stream of money and Clara had already planned her first outing in her new mink jacket.

CHAPTER NINETEEN

September 1944 – March 1945

The Dutch famine, known as the *Hongerwinter* (Hunger Winter), took place in the German-occupied part of the Netherlands, especially in the densely populated western provinces, during the winter of 1944-1945. A German blockade cut off food and fuel shipments from farm areas affecting millions of people. In the last phase of the war, over 18,000 Dutch people who had remained safe so far, died.

Jan Menton warmly welcomed the Biermans to his mother's home in the early hours of the morning of Sunday 3 September 1944. Cilla embraced him quickly and warmly just inside the house, away from prying eyes.

"Jan – oh, how wonderful to see you again! ... I'm so terribly sorry about your mother. How hard it must be for you!"

"Oh, Cilla – I can't tell you how much I will miss her."

"Yes, she was a very special and courageous woman."

"The saddest thing is that there is no time to even mourn for her," he said softly.

Still alive to the old dangers, Cilla and Edmund hurried down to the basement. The daily, dreary routine began again: darkness, hunger, silence and ... memories. The last time they had been in this basement was back in December 1942 when they came to hide with Cilla's father and step-mother. Where were they now? In the last twenty months not a day had gone by when she did not wonder.

Always, always, chief among Cilla's thoughts was news about her children. Jan was sorry but there was none. Spies and traitors had betrayed many underground activities and damaged the work of the Resistance. Some of his colleagues, as well as those in other networks, had been arrested and sent to concentration camps. Others had been executed. Shocked, Cilla wondered how they would have coped without Jan and the other Resistance workers.

During the winter of 1944 Dutch people died like flies as famine stalked the land. The winter was unusually harsh and the retreating German army destroyed docks and bridges to flood the country and impede the Allied advance. The destruction of the war ruined much of the country's agricultural land and strangled the transport of food stocks. By November 1944 the Nazis had lowered rations to a total of just 1000 grams per person per week. The result was widespread undernourishment, particularly in the densely populated cities of Amsterdam, Utrecht and Rotterdam. Then in December 1944 the ration was halved to 500 grams per person per week.

As food stocks in the Western Netherlands rapidly ran out, adult rations in Amsterdam dropped to new lows. Cilla and Edmund had spent the last few years getting used to decreasing amounts of food. The levels had now become intolerable.

They were skin and bones.

With the harshest Amsterdam winter she could ever remember, Cilla huddled in the freezing basement, wrapped in her fur jacket. The jacket, once a sign of luxury, with its faint scent of perfume deep within from an evening out many moons ago, was now becoming a necessity, to shield her from the bitter cold. After Clara's roaming eyes, Cilla was grateful she still owned it.

By February 1945 the ration had been lowered further to a life-threatening 350 calories per day. There was also neither coal nor wood. The freezing conditions and malnutrition drove people to desperate measures. Valuables were traded for tulip bulbs, the new staple ingredient to avoid starvation. Jan now brought them Darwin tulip bulbs. Instead of flower pots the beautiful tulips ended up in cooking pots. They ate them fried in oil to ease digestion.

Stories reached them about people dying of hunger in the streets. The number of deaths swelled as each day passed. Cilla worried about her husband. A mouse could barely survive on these minuscule potato and bread rations, much less a man of his medium-sized build.

And what of her children? If they had indeed survived the war, could they survive this famine? By March 1945 it was Edmund worrying about Cilla. She was as thin as a rake and had no energy. She was fading away in front of him. Worst of all, for the first time during this long war, she was giving up hope.

They were sitting on the paper-thin mattress in the dark basement in the middle of the day, a small candle their only source of light. They had just finished eating bitter tulip bulbs alongside a slither of bread and a cup of water. She pressed her hands against her stomach. Eating the bulbs was causing her so much pain. Edmund tried to comfort her by giving her words of encouragement.

"Cilenku, my darling. You must not give up now. We are so close to victory."

"It's not the first time I've heard this. Didn't we believe that last year when the allies came to liberate the South? Then we thought it would be any day. And the days rolled into weeks and the weeks have rolled into months. We have no idea when we will be free."

"I know. But now we are truly close, I feel it."

"I am trying to be positive. But I am so tired ... And the hunger and the pain from eating the flowers is crushing me," her voice trailed off, "I am so tired of hoping, hoping, hoping. I don't know how much longer I can last."

"You must. We have come so far. You cannot give up or give in now," he said, his voice cracking. "Do it for me. Do it for us. Do it for our children."

Her children. Where were they? How were they? Were they still alive? What if they were not? Her frail body shivered. Cilla looked at her husband. In the dim light his eyes glistened with tears. Yes, they had been through so much together. She would persevere, at the very least, to give him the courage to continue.

CHAPTER TWENTY

5 – 10 May 1945

The Dutch Famine ended with the liberation of the Western Netherlands on 5 May 1945 by the Canadian forces. It was three days before the complete surrender of Germany, following the suicide of Hitler. The 8 May 1945 marked Victory in Europe Day – "V-E Day". The Nazi regime, that had believed it would reign for one thousand years, had finally come to an end after twelve years.

Life was surreal, a black and white movie in slow motion. People were shell-shocked, numb from the physical and emotional pain and suffering they had endured for so long. Beautiful Amsterdam, the picture-perfect city of canals and tulips, was no longer beautiful. Instead, many survivors came home to find their city in tatters, their homes occupied by strangers or looted and their families gone. Amsterdam had been wrecked to the core. More profoundly, the soul of the city had been blighted by terror and occupation.

Cilla and Edmund emerged from the basement weak and gaunt. Lack of daylight and food, together with constant, nagging fear and flashes of panic had taken their toll on the young couple. Still only in their thirties they looked haggard and frail. They were lucky to emerge alive. If it had not been for the Allied food droppings in the last critical week they may not have survived.

Their days in hiding – almost nine hundred.
The days of not seeing their children – almost one thousand.

They needed to rebuild their strength and health. They were immediately sent to a hospital for shelter and food – joining hundreds of other survivors in the crowded wards.

Slowly they returned to life. Every moment brought a fresh sensation: the taste of fruit, the warmth of real woollen blankets, mattresses that soothed their aching bodies, the sound of birdsong in the spring air. Every new sensation a miracle.

Then, after a couple of days, they were faced with the traumatic task of finding their children and searching for survivors from their family. Who was alive and who was dead?

The Nazi plan for world domination ran alongside its objective to kill all the Jews in the biggest killing machines of all time. Since January 1945 the barbarity of the Nazis had become apparent for the world to see as the Allied soldiers liberated the hundreds of concentration camps throughout Europe.

The first concentration camp to be liberated was Auschwitz in Poland on 27 January 1945 by the Red Army. The last was Mauthausen in Austria, which was liberated on 5 May by the US Army.

The sickening evidence emerged of the wholesale mass murder of European Jews: killed in concentration camps, extermination camps, gas chambers, ovens, crematoria, mass graves and through death marches, forced labour, shooting, starvation, drowning, freezing, beating and disease.

And for those walking skeletons who miraculously still had a heart beat – and had not died of malnutrition or typhoid or typhus fever upon liberation – they had been robbed forever of their former lives. After what they suffered and witnessed, normal life was impossible. It was now about surviving or merely existing. Some would pick up their shattered lives somehow, but many would not. They could not.

A rare few summoned the strength and courage to turn their horrific experiences into life-long missions. One of the survivors of the last camp to be liberated – Mauthausen – was a thirty-six-year-old man called Simon Wiesenthal. He spent the rest of his life hunting Nazi war criminals.

The Red Cross had set up tables outside Amsterdam Central Station to register and help survivors. It was strange not to have to be afraid anymore. Cilla's aching bones yearned for the sun more than anything. She stood in the spring sunshine, her eyes closed. The warmth had a deliriously magical effect on her, after all those stifling, dark years in hiding. She breathed in deeply. The radiant sunshine suddenly sent her thoughts back a decade earlier to May 1935, when she was basking in the sun in the courtyard of the synagogue, where she had just met Edmund for the first time. Life then was so sweet and the future had looked so bright. Who could have predicted the hell that would follow?

Survivors were registered with two crucial words: "RETURNED ALIVE". Edmund and Cilla were among the few truly fortunate ones to appear on this list. Cilla scanned her eyes to see if her father and step-mother Chaim and Maria Schiff and Edmund's uncle Pinkus Friedmann were on it. They were not. She looked again for any other familiar names. There were none.

Jan Menton was a huge help when it came to finding out about the children. While some survivors had to wait weeks or months for information he used his intricate knowledge of the underground system to find out the fate of Renata and Anton quickly. After a few agonizingly long days he came to the hospital to deliver the news. Cilla and Edmund were physically and emotionally exhausted. They lay listlessly on the hospital beds, gazing blankly at the ceiling. Cilla lowered her eyes and saw Jan coming through the ward.

She clutched her husband's wrist in the bed next to hers. Jan had the news they had been desperately searching. Jan smiled encouragingly. Was that to soften the blow? During every painful experience she had endured in the long war her heart had never pounded as it did now. Her children were the only reason she had survived this brutal war. Were they alive? Or were they not? Her heart was thumping fast. They got up quickly to face the news. Cilla gripped Edmund's hand.

"My friends I have come to tell you that ..." he paused as he composed himself. "That ... that both Renata and Anton are alive and safe."

Did he say "alive and safe?" She could not be sure. Her mind was playing tricks. "What did you say?" she urged.

"Both Renata and Anton are alive and safe," he said stressing each word clearly.

Jan's eyes welled with tears. Bringing good news to this

honourable couple was the best thing to happen to him in a long time. Edmund embraced his wife. They held each other for a long time. Then Cilla looked up and brought Jan into the fold. Their sobs were silent.

Jan had traced Anton to a family outside the city. Now that the survival of his parents had been confirmed the young boy would be brought by Jan to the hospital. When, asked Cilla? Later today. Could it be true? Was she really going to see her son in a matter of hours – after an absence of hours, weeks, months and years?

Jan told them that Renata was happily settled with a couple in a city a few miles away. They had brought her up as their own child as they did not have their own children. Getting her back, he explained, would need to be handled very sensitively. Her foster parents and the little girl had become very attached to each other.

At a time when so many Dutch children and their parents had been sent to the gas chambers, they were the lucky ones. Cilla was getting her children back and her children were getting their parents back – a combination few were fortunate enough to enjoy.

The eight-year-old boy who entered the hospital waiting room that evening was as thin and gaunt as a ghost. But there was no mistaking his trademark shiny black hair and beautiful blue eyes. Cilla gasped as she felt the touch of his face and drew her trembling fingers through his hair. She embraced him as if she would never let him go again. Still very weak, Edmund summoned all his strength to lift his only son in the air, to hold him tight and never let him go.

CHAPTER TWENTY-ONE

May – June 1945

Rebuilding their lives happened slowly, bit by bit. Anton slept in a bed between his parents in the hospital. He was very quiet. Cilla sensed his time away had probably been traumatic. She watched him fall asleep at night and stared at him for hours. She touched him in the middle of the night to ensure he was still there. Having him wake up next to her every morning was nothing short of a miracle.

After a week recuperating, Cilla felt it was time to go and be reunited with her daughter. Again she felt guilty. So many survivors did not have the good fortune to make such plans.

Having had time to think about the situation she realised that it would be wholly unfair on her daughter to pull her abruptly away from a loving home. First they would visit her, gradually rebuilding their relationship with her. Cilla believed she would need to earn the right to take her home – only after Renata showed she was ready to leave the place she currently called home.

A meeting was made to visit the home of Valerie and Arnold

Resnel, the couple who had raised Renata all the time since she went into hiding in September 1942. Jan, who had become a firm friend of the family, stayed with Anton in the hospital.

Cilla and Edmund made their way to the town of Wormerveer. It was unbelievable that throughout their years in hiding their daughter had been living just ten miles outside Amsterdam. After a train journey and a short walk on foot in the pleasant spring sun they arrived at the house. The Resnels lived in a modern, detached-brick, 1930's house on the edge of the town. In front was a neatly-tended garden with a deep red rose bush next to a flowerbed brimming with a sea of pink and red tulips. Cilla's immediate thought was how happy she was for her daughter to be raised in such a setting.

They walked nervously up the garden path and knocked lightly on the front door. The door was opened quickly by a tall, well-built man and a motherly-looking woman. Their faces seemed friendly but anxious. A beautiful Dutch Shepherd dog was visible in the background.

The two couples gazed at each other and said nothing for a few long seconds. Cilla stepped forward and embraced Valerie warmly. They had never met before but they shared a beautiful gift – a beloved child who would bond them now and forever. Silent tears trickled down their faces. For Cilla they were tears of huge sorrow for the loss of her child for so long, mixed with relief that this charming woman had been entrusted to look after Renata. For Valerie it was loving a child, who had given them so much happiness. They had been childless for twenty years. Giving Renata back was too painful to even contemplate.

They were led through the hallway and into a bright,

immaculate kitchen. In the middle of the room was a round glass table with four chairs. On it stood a vase of freshly cut pink and red tulips. Cilla's heart was racing, her hands shaking. Her eyes scanned the kitchen and then looked out of the window ahead. She opened her mouth in disbelief. She tapped Edmund so that he could share what she saw. Out there, in a tree-lined garden sat a little girl on a swing, swinging energetically. Cilla had to restrain herself from running out and smothering her in kisses. Edmund gripped her wrist to stop her doing anything impulsive. She looked on intently, taking everything in. The shoulder length wavy dark hair, the almond-shaped eyes, the round face, the smile. Yes, it was Renata. How big she had grown! How pretty she looked ... but much more importantly ... how happy. Cilla's heart skipped a beat. She took Edmund's hand and hugged him tightly, silently weeping. Their daughter was safe and well ... and she would be coming home soon.

Valerie and Arnold looked on helplessly. The Resnels had grown to love Renata as if she were their own, especially as they had not been able to have children of their own. They had agreed to look after Renata out of compassion – because they were good Christians and could not bear the racial hatred and persecution of the Jews. They had not envisaged how much they would love this child and how heartbreaking it would be to give her back. They now feared their lives would be empty. It seemed that having and losing her was worse than never having had her in the first place.

In fact by this point they had known, raised and loved Renata for longer than her birth parents. The Biermans had given her up when she was almost twenty months old, while the Resnels had her for thirty-two months – more than two and a half long years.

They had always known what the arrangement was and knew this day could come. It had just come far too soon. And the pain was more painful than they could ever have imagined.

The moment had come for Cilla to be reunited with her beloved daughter. The moment had come for Valerie to be emotionally torn from her. Valerie went out through the kitchen door and into the garden, holding an ice-lolly. The others followed. She turned to Cilla, "Do you want to give it to Renata?"

"Thank you," she said appreciatively.

The four of them walked up to the swing, Valerie leading the way. Renata looked up in bewilderment. She brought the swing to a halt and whispered, "Aunty Valerie, who are those people?"

"They are our friends." There was a long pause. "They have come to visit us from Amsterdam."

"Oh," said Renata.

Valerie stepped back and pointed to the couple, "This is Cilla and Edmund." She turned to the four-year-old girl and announced proudly, "and this is ... Renata."

Cilla felt choked. Her hands were shaking. It took all her strength to speak. "Hello darling," she said gently, "would you like an ice-lolly?"

"Hello," Renata said. She took it shyly, "thank you."

Cilla stepped up closer and smoothed her daughter's shiny hair. Edmund went up and touched her cheek. That was enough for now. Anything more affectionate would have made the little girl uncomfortable.

The couple stepped back. They were rooted to the spot, unable to take their eyes off her. Their daughter was in a world of her own. She had resumed swinging, blissfully content and oblivious to all the attention she was attracting. They examined her delicate features – arched eyebrows, bottle green eyes, flecked with gold, pearly baby teeth, delicate lips.

They had missed her gradual transition from baby to girl. There in front of them, in one minute she had been transformed from their memory of her as a baby into a perfect princess.

The two couples returned to the kitchen. They sat down at the glass table. Valerie poured everyone a glass of water and served them cut fruit. Cilla was still trembling. After drinking a glass of water she slowly relaxed. There was a lot to discuss. She wanted to know so much about the past two and a half years. How had her daughter coped when she arrived? How had her life been ever since?

The Resnels had told everyone that Renata was Arnold's brother's daughter from Rotterdam. When the city was bombed in May 1941 many children were evacuated and sent to live with relatives. She was thus called Renata Resnel and had false identification papers made up accordingly. Those who did not ask, like people in the street, assumed the girl was the couple's own daughter.

But her arrival at their home had at first been fraught with difficulty. When she arrived in September 1942 Renata cried non-stop. The first month was very challenging as the baby was very sad. But soon after that it got better each day and after about three months she settled down. She eventually integrated well into the local kindergarten and made friends. She also became very close to their dog Amstel who actually had been a great comfort during the initial difficult period.

Cilla listened intently, digesting all this information with difficulty. She asked Valerie about Renata's favourite foods. They were spaghetti and cheese, bread and butter, yellow cheese, milk, and she loved apples. Cilla made a mental note.

The conversation moved to the all important issue of how to handle the situation now. Despite her almost unbearable desire to walk away with her daughter immediately, Cilla knew it was not wise or fair and indeed would be counterproductive. She recommended to the Resnels that it would be in the child's best interest to meet her and Edmund gradually before she went back to live with them permanently. After all they were now mere strangers and that would be very scary and overwhelming for such a young child. The Resnels agreed and invited them to visit as often as they wanted – until Renata would eventually feel comfortable to leave with them. In spite of their sincere wish to reunite this family, they hoped the process would last a long time so they could enjoy the little girl for as long as possible.

Cilla was shaking as she left the Resnel's home. Although she was genuinely relieved that her daughter had been so well looked after she hadn't properly contemplated that this honourable couple would adore and … love, yes, love her so very much. She saw it in the way they looked at her and in the way they spoke to her. She shivered. She knew how they felt and she knew what they were going to feel when it was time to hand her over. Afterall, she had been through the same with the same child. Moreover, how could Renata be expected to leave such a loving home? There was a long journey ahead fraught with anguish, confusion and sadness. It was all so unjust.

Edmund tried to reassure her that her feelings were normal and it was far better that their daughter was loved than the alternative scenarios, which would have resulted in a much uglier situation. How much luckier they were than those parents who had not survived the war, and whose children were now left permanently with foster-parents. How much luckier they were than those parents who had returned, so physically and emotionally shattered that they could no longer care for their children. How much luckier they were than those parents who, whether or not they survived, had lost their children to the foster-parents or institutions which had had the children baptised. Yes, she knew he was right but still she sobbed all the way home at the utter injustice of a situation where there could be no winners.

Cilla and Edmund came to visit the Resnels every Friday and Sunday afternoon for over a month, each time bringing a small gift for Renata and another for the Resnels. With the patience of a saint Cilla was determined not to rush anything until she knew in her heart of hearts that her daughter was as ready as she could be.

"We've waited this long," she told her husband, "we can and will wait a bit longer."

They also decided not to take Anton with them on the visits. He was still deeply affected by his time in hiding and needed to deal with life slowly. He would meet his sister again when she eventually returned home.

CHAPTER TWENTY-TWO

June 1945

The atmosphere on the streets of Amsterdam was gloomy. Survivors were searching desperately for loved ones and waiting for news. The newspaper reports gave more and more details of the concentration camps and the wholesale massacre of the Jews.

Cilla and Edmund were often kept awake at night in the hospital by the wailing of those suffering nightmares or having their worst fears confirmed – discovering that their son, daughter, sister, brother, mother or father had been sent to a concentration camp – and would never be coming home.

The Biermans were desperate to find out about their own families. Edmund had heard that many people from his home town of Spisske Podhradie had been murdered in Majdanek concentration camp in 1942. As each day, week and month passed without news he held out little hope for the survival of his sister, brother and father, and other family members, who had still been living in their home town at the outbreak of the war.

Cilla was frantic to find news about her father and step-mother. It was becoming more and more apparent that they had not survived the rest of the war in hiding – or else they would have surely shown up by now. Instead, they had probably been sent to a concentration camp. When were they caught? To which one were they sent? Had they survived? Many questions. No answers.

There were stories of husbands and wives coming back to Amsterdam alone wondering about the fate of their spouses. Many couples had been separated from each other in the vast concentration camp of Auschwitz. Looking for any scrap of information they would ask other Auschwitz survivors if they had seen their spouse in the concentration camp: When? Where? What did he, she say? Often a witness would confirm the worst. Yes, they had seen him, her ... before their deaths ... before they were sent to the gas chamber.

As each day passed Cilla heard more and more horror stories – more and more names of old friends, acquaintances and neighbours who had been murdered. It was just a bare clinical fact – that some time in the last three years a known person had been killed. There was no period of mourning, no time for grieving, no tombstone, no burial place, no body. Nothing.

One Friday in June on their return from the twice-weekly trip to the Resnels, as the train slowly pulled into Amsterdam Central station, Cilla looked across at the platform ahead. A train stood stationary. Its doors were open and a strange array of people were emerging slowly from it. Cilla covered her mouth in shocked disbelief.

It was a scene out of the *Inferno*. Emaciated skeletons, scraps of skin clinging to their bones, limped, hobbled, staggered down the platform. They were staring ahead, some leaning on others for support. Rags hung from their pitiful bodies, their hair cropped or bald. Hundreds of them were aimlessly wandering down the platform, lifeless and soulless, suffering from malnutrition, disease, exhaustion. They had returned to Amsterdam Central Station after having been deported from that same station just a few years earlier. They had left as humans and returned from Auschwitz, Belsen, Sobibor and Theresienstadt as skeletons.

A surge of hope suddenly rose in Cilla's heart and she scanned the crowds eagerly for her father of whom she still had no news. He would have been sixty but she knew he might well have looked ninety if he had been in a concentration camp. She strained her eyes, looking at every elderly-looking person. They all looked haggard and old and she noticed some were wearing odd shoes. And it was almost impossible to distinguish man from woman. When her train, in the parallel platform, came to a halt she jumped out. She sprinted the length of the platform and down the stairs. Edmund hurried after her. They arrived outside the big station. The skeletons came out of the station to the shock and horror of the passers-by. The survivors inched very slowly to the tables manned by the Red Cross. Desperately, Cilla searched the queues lining up in front of the tables. But, no, her father was not there.

Cilla was aghast. Her survival of the war had been torture. But, in comparison to what she now saw, she realised God really had been with her.

CHAPTER TWENTY-THREE

July 1945

Amongst all the tragedy very occasionally there was some good news. Edmund had heard that his older brother Usher, together with his wife Pearl and two young children, had survived in London.

But Usher did not know of Edmund's fate. Edmund also did not know the fate of their younger brother Shia.

Edmund sent an urgent telegram to Usher in Dutch. It said: "I, MY WIFE AND CHILDREN HAVE BEEN SPARED. WHERE IS SHIA?"

He anxiously awaited the response.

In the meantime Cilla continued to visit the Resnels and Renata twice-weekly. She put on a brave face as she did not want her sadness and grief to affect the process of being reunited with her daughter.

By the end of June Renata was actually looking forward to the visits from the charming couple who doted on her. A special bond had now been created between them and Cilla did not want to lose the momentum. On the last Friday in June, as the four adults sat in the kitchen, Cilla broached the subject. She picked her words carefully:

"Valerie, I think Renata looks ready," she stopped there. There was no need to complete the sentence.

Valerie looked at Arnold. Her eyes were brimming with tears. The words came out before she could stop them. She had clearly been thinking about them for a long time, "Please leave Renata with us. You are young and you can have another child. We cannot. She is our only child."

Cilla gasped. She covered her face with her hands. The words shocked her to the core. Both husbands embraced their trembling wives. A few minutes passed. Cilla wiped her eyes and looked up. She leaned over to Valerie, sitting across the table from her, and took her hands in hers. Her voice was strangely clear and composed, "Let our daughter return with us. She is our flesh and blood. We have desperately dreamed of her return. We survived this terrible war because of her and her brother. We will pray for you to have your own child."

The following week they picked up their daughter Renata once and for all. She was told that Aunty Valerie and Uncle Arnold were going away for a long business trip and the Biermans were going to look after her in their home in Amsterdam. They made it sound like an adventure and Renata happily agreed to go with them.

Renata was excited about going to the capital city of Amsterdam. During the war she had never visited the city but had heard so much about this "beautiful place". She sat on the train wide-eyed, happily eating a sandwich. After the sandwich

Cilla offered her a bar of chocolate. For now her priority was to smother her with affection before she would mother her with love.

CHAPTER TWENTY-FOUR

July 1945

Edmund's colleague from the fur industry, Heinz Bork had survived the war with his family. Upon liberation he immediately went in search of his old Jewish friends the Biermans. To his sheer amazement he found Edmund and Cilla alive and recuperating in the hospital. He broke down in tears of joy when he heard the children had survived too.

The couple was so happy to see him again. Old faces meant so much when so many had died. He became a huge pillar of support in helping the family get back on their feet.

After building up their strength at the hospital the Biermans went in search of renting a new home. Cilla and Edmund decided that living in their old home on Plantage Parklaan would bring back too many bad memories so they opted for a new terraced house on Sarphatistraat – coincidentally also number 24 – a short distance away from their old home. It was not as elegant as their first home but it was spacious. More importantly, it was a fresh new start. They moved in at the beginning of July.

Renata stepped into the new house on Sarphatistraat. She looked around curiously.

"Shall I show you your room darling?" Cilla asked.

"Yes please," she said happily.

They climbed the stairs and walked into the room with the pink door. In it was a bed, a dressing table, a huge teddy bear, a blackboard and chalks. Any spare money, of which there was very little, had gone into this bedroom. Her parents saw it as an all-important investment and they used her bedroom at the Resnel's home for inspiration. Valerie had told them that she loved to brush her hair by the dressing table and draw on the blackboard. Cilla knew her room was to be her sanctuary and it needed to be special and comfortable. Renata looked pleased.

Anton finally met his sister. He shook her hand and looked at her with curiosity. He, of course, was told not to disclose that he was her brother. Renata was tired. It had been a long day and a tiring journey. By 6 p.m. she was rubbing her eyes.

"Let's quickly have a glass of milk and then you can have a bath and go to bed."

Renata sat in the small kitchen sipping the warm milk, curiously taking everything in around her. It was a simple room but clean and functional. When she finished the drink Cilla took her upstairs to have a quick bath and get ready for bed. Renata put on her pink pyjamas and then she pulled out an old doll from her suitcase – it was her favourite doll, Kitty. Oh my, thought Cilla, it was the one I gave her before she left us. It had survived the war and returned "home" with it's owner. Cilla had to compose herself. Her daughter was waiting for her.

"Off to bed now darling," she said pulling the pale pink blanket off the bed and waiting for her to crawl in. Instead, Renata went to the bottom of the bed, knelt down, closed her eyes, put her hands together and recited a bedtime prayer:

Our Father, who art in heaven,
hallowed be thy Name,
thy kingdom come,
thy will be done,
on earth as it is in heaven.

Give us this day our daily bread.
And forgive us our trespasses,
as we forgive those
who trespass against us.

And lead us not into temptation,
but deliver us from evil.

For thine is the kingdom,
and the power, and the glory,
for ever and ever. Amen.

Cilla stared in disbelief. She was numb and had a lump in her throat. Her Jewish daughter had just recited a Christian bedtime prayer. She did not trust herself to say anything so kept silent. Renata climbed into bed content. "Good night Cilla."

Trembling, Cilla tried to control her emotions. She leaned over and tucked the little girl in. As utterly shocked as she was she did not want to spoil this moment for which she had waited an eternity. My daughter has returned home at last. She is alive, healthy, happy, beautiful – let me enjoy it. New challenges will be dealt with on a new day. She kissed her daughter's forehead for a very long time. It had been nearly three years since she had tucked her daughter in and nothing was going to spoil this long-awaited moment. Nothing.

The next morning there was more. As the four of them sat down for breakfast Renata put her hands together and recited the Christian blessing. *"For this and all we are about to receive, make us truly grateful, Lord. Through Christ we pray. Amen."*

Edmund and Cilla were wide-eyed. Somehow they had not expected this either. And so before every meal she said the blessing and before every bedtime she recited the prayer. They realised that getting their daughter back to Judaism was going to be far more of a challenge than they had anticipated.

The days were long and filled to the brim. Cilla wanted to spend every possible moment with her daughter. Yes, she absolutely wanted to make up for the time she had lost seeing her daughter grow up. But also she needed to keep Renata so positively preoccupied that there was little risk of her becoming homesick for the Resnels.

Cilla had plenty to do in the aftermath of the long war but it would have to wait. For now her daughter was a priority. She invented her own curriculum. She played with Renata in the garden, pushed her on the swing they had just bought, or sat with her, colouring picture books and reading to her. After the quiet simplicity of country life, the liveliness of Amsterdam captivated the excited little girl. On walks through the city, Renata was enchanted by the colourful, grand terraced houses, the hum of life, the bustle of the markets, and the stately barges lining the canals.

Every evening Renata had her bath before bedtime – and prayer time. Cilla had decided that the best way forward was to do nothing for now. Too much change this early on could be damaging. Every evening the ritual returned like clockwork. Her daughter would kneel, close her eyes, put her hands together and peacefully recite the Christian bedtime prayer. For a deeply committed Jewish mother it was painful but she waited patiently.

Meanwhile Edmund spent a lot of time with Anton – walking and talking or keeping him company as he read a book. In the evenings when Renata was asleep, Cilla devoted her time to being with her son as much as possible.

She understood that he had not been treated well during his time in hiding and talking about it added to the pain. She bore this knowledge with a heavy heart and hoped time and love would be a healer.

August 1945

Cilla had waited thirty-five months – or to be precise one hundred and fifty Sabbaths – to celebrate the Friday night Sabbath with her family again. Unlike so many grieving Jews, whose families had been wiped out, she felt truly grateful. The four silver candlesticks, the only remnants of her former life, along with a few other personal possessions, had been kept safe by Heinz Bork. Her hands trembled as she lit the candles. She closed her eyes and blessed the flickering flames.

"Dear God," she whispered, "thank you for watching over us and thank you for reuniting us with our beloved children." Her eyes were closed for a long time. She did not forget her final prayer, "Dear God, please, oh please bless Valerie and Arnold Resnel with a baby."

Renata looked at her mother curiously. "What are you doing?"

Cilla answered cautiously. "I am blessing the candles so we can enjoy a delicious meal together. We do it every Friday night."

The Friday night meal was an overwhelmingly spiritual

event. Four individuals, one family, split apart by their harrowing experiences – but finally reunited. Despite food rationing Cilla had managed to put together a traditional meal reminiscent of the old days. She glanced at her children. Anton was subdued, eating slowly. Edmund looked deep in thought. Renata was happily picking at her food, enjoying the new tastes of chicken soup, roast chicken and potatoes. Cilla's joy was shot through with grief for the lost years and the father she now knew she would never see again.

The war had shattered everything. A beautiful family picture had been blasted to smithereens and was now being stuck back together – bit by tiny bit. But it could not and would never be a seamless picture again. The cracks were still there, invisible below the surface.

They were lost souls who had been reunited. The treasured family picture of the Bierman family – taken in 1938 in Edmund's home town of Spisske Podhradie – before the larger family had been destroyed, stood on the mantelpiece, a reminder of the life that once was, long, long ago.

On Sunday morning Renata was playing in her bedroom when the church bells began pealing through the city. Hearing the chimes, she jumped up and peered through the window at the church spire in the distance. "Cilla," she cried. Cilla appeared in the doorway.

"What's the matter, darling?"

"Did you hear the bells?"

"Yes, they're lovely."

"Are we going?"

Cilla's heart skipped a beat. "Going where?" she asked calmly.

"To church."

Cilla breathed in deeply, "Let me speak to Edmund darling." She left, quite unsure how to handle this new challenge.

They decided to take Renata by tram to the *Posthoornkerk*, a majestic neo-gothic church designed by the architect Pierre Cuypers in the 1800s. It was far enough to justify not doing it often and impressive enough to make it a sort of sight-seeing trip for Anton. It was the best compromise with which they could come up.

CHAPTER TWENTY-SIX

September 1945

Usher was overjoyed to receive the telegram in his home in London announcing Edmund's survival. Because his understanding of Dutch was limited, he assumed the Dutch word *gespaard* (spared) was similar to a Yiddish word meaning imprisoned. Nonetheless, imprisoned meant his brother and family were alive. His joy was as boundless as his surprise.

Usher in turn informed Edmund that, thank God, Shia had survived the long war too. It was a miracle that three brothers had survived.

Shia had gone to England and volunteered in the 1st Czechoslovak Independent Armoured Brigade Group. This was a unit of expatriate Czechoslovaks, organised and equipped by the UK in 1943. In August 1944 the brigade landed in Normandy and was given the mission of containing the German-held port of Dunkirk until the German surrender in May 1945.

It was in England that he met the beautiful seventeen-year-old Fay Tannenbaum, who worked at his brother Usher's battery business. The dashing couple married in London in 1943. As soon as Shia heard that Edmund was alive he hurried over to Amsterdam with a suitcase full of clothes. The two brothers wept in each others' arms for a long time.

By September 1945 Shia and Fay had moved to Brussels, just a few hours' drive from Amsterdam. Edmund and Cilla welcomed the news that the young couple was moving so close to them with genuine delight. One could not take for granted family during these troubled times. Cilla and Edmund continuously mourned the loss of so many people. Reunion with anyone who had survived the war was a blessing, how much more so an adored younger brother.

Cilla met her new twenty-year-old sister-in-law for the first time. The two women forged an instant connection. Fay respected Cilla and marvelled at how she had rebuilt her home and family with such strength and passion. Moreover, she was amazed at how sensitively she dealt with the predicament regarding her daughter. She looked at her older sister-in-law in awe. She was the ultimate survivor.

When Fay and Shia visited for the Sabbath, instead of coming with gifts of chocolate and flowers they brought a real, and most unusual delicacy – carp, the fish used to make the traditional Eastern European Jewish gefilte fish. It was boiled and then combined with egg, breadcrumbs and grated onion before being poached into dumplings. The fish was then enjoyed as a first course, served cold with a spoonful of deep crimson strong horseradish sauce.

It seemed that some aspects of life were returning to relative normality in post-war Amsterdam. But it did not take much to remind Cilla of the horrors. The sound of screeching tyres in the street would be enough to make her freeze and think of flight. Or she would recoil from standing by the window – forgetting that there were no longer traitors or Nazis lying in wait for her.

Eventually Cilla and Edmund reconnected with the people they had met or who had looked after them in hiding. Chief amongst them were Hans and Ella Bok and Lilly Frankel who had survived the war. Lilly was eternally grateful to Cilla for having the wisdom and foresight to change her identity just in time to save her and her baby. Their mutual war-time experiences would make them lifelong friends – or rather, soul mates.

And closer to home there was other good news. Edmund's brother and sister-in-law in London, Usher and Pearl, had just had their third child, a son, Shalom on 22 September 1945. In the aftermath of the war the family legacy continued.

CHAPTER TWENTY-SEVEN

September 1945

Renata initially adapted well to her new home and family. She was curious and adventurous and enjoyed the attention and treats she received. But a few weeks in, after the novelty had worn off, she started pining for aunty Valerie and uncle Arnold. Repeatedly, fretfully, she demanded to know when they would be returning from their trip.

Feeling uncomfortable, Cilla explained gently that the Resnels had been delayed abroad for a bit longer. Renata became sullen and withdrawn. One morning Cilla was surprised to find that she had still not woken up by her usual 7 a.m. Half an hour later Cilla went into her bedroom to check on her. She sat on the edge of the bed and gently nudged her daughter.

"Renata darling, it's time to get up."

Renata's eyes were closed.

"Renata," she nudged again. "We have a lot to do today."

The little girl still did not open her eyes. Cilla was growing alarmed. "Darling, are you okay?"

"No," came the whisper.

"What's the matter, my darling?"

Renata opened her eyes slowly, tears glistening. "Aunty Valerie and uncle Arnold don't love me anymore."

Cilla breathed in deeply, "Of course they do. They love you with all their heart."

"So why have they left me?"

"Darling, they haven't left you."

"They have. In the night I dreamt they were in a huge boat sailing away from me."

Cilla put a hand on her mouth.

The little girl continued. "They've left me. They're not coming back." Her voice wavered. "They even took Amstel."

"Who?"

"Our dog, Amstel our dog," she wept, the tears flowing now without restraint. "I miss them so much!"

The words caused Cilla so much agony. She drew her daughter's hair away from her face, wiped her tears and smoothed her cheeks. Renata closed her eyes again.

"My darling, aunty Valerie and uncle Arnold have never loved anyone more than you," faltered Cilla. "I promise you. And they never wanted to leave you in the first place. Really they did not. But they were not allowed to take a little girl with them. They just couldn't. They miss you so much. They love you so much."

Renata's eyes remained closed. Cilla continued slowly, "As soon as they can, they will see you. I will find out when. Okay? ... Darling is that okay?

"Yes."

"But for now we have a lot to do today ... You know where we are going? ... I'm taking you to the biggest, most beautiful place in the whole wide world. It has an aquarium filled with beautiful fish and lots and lots of amazing animals."

Renata opened her eyes. "Are we going to the zoo?" she whispered.

"Yes we are ... But if you don't hurry up they may sell all the tickets."

Cilla left the bedroom still trembling. She had been warned about this and now she had to deal with it.

Visiting the Artis Zoo was not going to be easy. It was an impulse, to distract Renata from her sadness. The zoo had been Cilla's favourite haunt when Anton was a baby but she had not been back since 1940. It belonged to a lost time, a time that could never be regained. She had never dreamed of returning to a place that had been "Forbidden to Jews". But in recent months, as more details of the war emerged, she had heard a strange, startling story. Around a dozen Jews had been hidden in the zoo, along with several hundred Dutch non-Jews desperate to avoid being sent to forced labour in Germany.

One story haunted Cilla – that of a young Jewish woman and a little Jewish boy who had been hidden by the zoo keeper above the lion and tiger den, in the alcoves used to store hay. Cramped in a low-ceilinged shed for many months, they froze in the winter nights and burned in the unbearably hot summer days. They had survived on the food provided for the animals. Somehow this knowledge made returning to the zoo easier. Perhaps, it was time to move on. But it was going to be hard.

The resplendent grounds, filled with exotic animals and fragrant flower gardens were as enchanting as Cilla remembered. Renata's face lit up with excitement as they moved from cage to cage, smiling at the parrots, toucans and cockatoos. At the lion's den Renata gazed in wonder at the mighty creatures. Cilla looked up at the alcoves above the cages trying to imagine how those fugitives had survived the confinement, the hunger, the cold, the blazing heat, the fear. Yes, she could absolutely taste their fear.

An hour later, Cilla took Renata to the coffee shop for an ice-lolly. In the queue, they were absorbed in chatting about their favourite animals. Suddenly, as if out of the air, a frail old woman stood in front of Cilla. She had cropped white hair, a deep scar running down her left cheek bone. Her front teeth were missing.

"Hello ... Cilla?"

Cilla looked at the stranger closely. The woman's eyes were wild.

"Cilla Bierman?" she repeated.

"Yes, it is Cilla. But ... I am so sorry Madame – please remind me who you are."

"I am Marion Schindler, Cilla – it is me, Marion."

Cilla gasped. Marion was a young woman, younger than Cilla. She could not be much older than thirty. They had befriended each other at Anton's kindergarten. Marion had two daughters – Simona and Sarah. Simona was Anton's age and Sarah two years younger. Cilla could not conceal her disbelief and immense sadness as she looked at the transformed woman. The last time she had seen her, Marion's hair had been light brown, shoulder length. Her smile had been vibrant with life and joy.

Just then it was Cilla's turn to be served. Her hands shook as she paid for Renata's ice lolly. She told the little girl to sit on the plastic chair in the shade. She wanted to speak to Marion out of earshot of her daughter.

Marion and her family and ninety-five-year-old grandmother had been deported to Auschwitz. She had returned alone. Her home was occupied by another family and she was now living with her late husband's old aunt in a one-bedroom apartment.

"Renata looks well. How did she survive the war?" she asked matter of factly.

"She was looked after by a special couple," said Cilla softly, embarrassed.

"Looked after," repeated Marion. "I wish someone had looked after my girls," she whispered.

Cilla's eyes focused on the tiny gravel pebbles at her feet.

"Simona and Sarah loved the zoo. I'm trying to imagine they're still here with me." Her eyes were vacant, glazed – as if she were in a dream. "Their favourite animals were the pelicans. They could stare at them for hours ... "

Cilla raised her eyes to meet the woman's face. As she did she saw her forearm – a six-digit number tattooed on it. The Nazis had tattooed numbers on the flesh of Auschwitz victims, a form of identification instead of using names. Cilla instantly saw the numbers 3, 5, 7, but the other numbers were a blur. She looked away quickly.

Marion's traumatised eyes hovered between sadness and delusion. The war had killed her, as surely as if she had been murdered in Auschwitz.

"Would you like to join us going around the zoo?" Cilla asked, hopelessly.

"No, I came to see the pelicans. I'm going now."

"What about a coffee? Let's sit and have a coffee in the sun," Cilla pressed.

"No, no ... There is no sun ... Not anymore."

Cilla and Renata returned home shortly after. The shock of seeing Marion was traumatic. Marion's face and the number tattooed on her arm shadowed her every thought. Those inky blue death camp digits. She couldn't stop thinking about them. Cilla needed all her strength to prevent herself spiralling into a deep depression over the next few days. She had to be strong for her daughter, who was suffering her own problems.

In spite of the fun at the zoo, Renata became listless and weary very soon after the visit. Cilla knew she must act quickly. She told Edmund she had an idea. She recalled how Valerie Resnel had said their dog Amstel had helped Renata in the early days. A dog could be the solution. It would probably do the family a lot of good.

A few days later a beautiful white Dutch shepherd dog joined the family. They named him Kees. Renata was fascinated by him and warmed to him immediately. She fed him and played with him for endless hours in the garden. From now on she would not go anywhere without her beloved companion.

The Jewish New Year fell shortly after the summer – on the 8 September. Cilla saw it as a good opportunity to tell her daughter about some "Jewish" customs, a term with which she was not yet familiar. As Renata helped her lay the table for the evening meal Cilla chatted casually. Jewish people, she told the little girl, said prayers in Hebrew and she would get to hear them tonight when they ate together and would recite the blessings. Tomorrow, she continued, she would take her to the place where everyone prays. Praying to God was an important part of all religions, explained

Cilla, but people just did it differently and in different places.

Renata listened as she helped Cilla lay the cutlery on the table. When they had finished, Renata looked up, "Cilla. It looks even more beautiful than on Friday night." Her mother smiled.

The next day Cilla took Renata to the Swammerdam Street Synagogue for the New Year service. Hand in hand she proudly walked through the streets with her daughter. It suddenly dawned on her that it was the first time that she had ever taken her to a synagogue. They arrived and went upstairs to the ladies' gallery. In the men's section below Renata excitedly spotted Anton sitting next to his father. Cilla stared at them for a long time. Her family was whole. Her eyes filled with tears again.

Cilla was relieved to be attending a new synagogue. She would not have been able to bear seeing the empty seats in the old synagogue of all those she had known who would never come home again. Here, in the solemn, dim atmosphere of the synagogue, she wondered whether she might ever, some day, begin to heal.

In front of her sat her new friend Pepi. She had been sent with her husband Moshe to Bergen Belsen from Westerbork. They had survived the war yet sickeningly, Moshe had died very soon after liberation from the typhoid fever which had ravaged thousands and thousands of weakened survivors. As Cilla looked around the synagogue everyone seemed lonely, old, grief stricken. And the sound of weeping was never far away.

At bedtime that night, Cilla stood by closely. After Renata had said her usual *Our Father*, her mother came up to her and motioned her to sit on the bed beside her, "Darling do you know how the Jewish bedtime prayer goes?"

"No."

"Let me tell you. We call it the *Shema*. Do you know we said it today in the synagogue? But we also say the first part at bedtime. It is a very important prayer that shows us how much we love God and that He is the only One to protect us. Shall we do a bit now? I will say one line and then you follow. OK?"

"OK."

"First cover your eyes with your right hand, before you start, so we can concentrate. OK darling?"

"OK."

"Kel Melech Ne'eman," started Cilla

"Kel Melech Ne'eman," repeated Renata slowly.

"Shema Yisrael."

"Shema Yisrael."

"Hashem Elokainu."

"Hashem Elokainu."

"Hashem Echad."

"Hashem Echad."

"Good girl darling, you said it beautifully."

"Thank you."

Cilla tucked Renata in bed and kissed her forehead, "Good night darling, I love you."

"Good night."

And so at the start of the Jewish New Year Renata started to become Jewish … all over again.

CHAPTER TWENTY-EIGHT

September – December 1945

Afticr the Jewish New Year Cilla enrolled Renata in a small local kindergarten. The little girl's days now had a structure. She also became best friends with a little girl called Karen. Renata came home each day happy and fulfilled. Anton was enrolled in the local Jewish school Rosh Pinah. He impressed his teachers with his studious habits, talents and thirst for knowledge.

Every night the new bedtime ritual took place. Renata said her *Our Father*, followed by the *Shema*. They went over old words and added a few more new words of the Hebrew prayer when she was ready. Like clockwork Cilla then tucked Renata in bed and kissed her forehead.

"Good night darling, I love you," she would say.

"Good night," Renata would respond.

It was the same for the blessings at meal times. Once Renata had finished her usual Christian blessing, Cilla would then tell her the Jewish one and the little girl would repeat it slowly.

As the weeks rolled on Renata accepted that the Resnels were not coming back for the time being. She busied herself with kindergarten or playing with Anton, Karen or Kees. And when she was not playing she was happy to help Cilla around the house.

A few weeks later Cilla celebrated her thirty-third birthday. She needed no presents – she had her children back. Nonetheless, Renata came home from kindergarten with an artistic creation of real autumn leaves stuck on paper. The crisp orange, red and yellow leaves merged together in a vibrant mirage of nature and colour. "Happy happy birthday, lots of love and kisses from Renata," said the message. Cilla could not contain her delight.

As October darkened into November and the days grew shorter there was a buzz in the streets about the impending arrival of Christmas. The people of Amsterdam counted down the days with zeal for their first proper Christmas since 1939. By mid-November the city was ablaze with colourful lights, Christmas trees and decorations in anticipation of the long awaited celebration – in freedom at last.

Cilla was happy that the Jewish festival of *Chanukah* would be a good distraction for her daughter, who might otherwise focus on the arrival of Christmas. The Jewish festival commemorated the rededication of the Second Temple in Jerusalem. It celebrated God's miracle of making the oil, used to light the *Menorah* (candelabra), last eight days instead of one. The eight-day festival was a family celebration, a time for eating oily delicacies and for giving and receiving gifts.

The first night of the festival fell on Thursday night 29 November 1945. The family crowded around the eight branched *Menorah* by the window sill. After spending years hiding away from windows so as not to be seen, it still seemed strange to be allowed to celebrate this Jewish festival freely. The flickering light illuminated the subdued and thoughtful faces of Edmund, Cilla and Anton. But it also illuminated the smiling, curious face of little Renata, who was captivated by the new experience.

After the blessings, songs, and the tasty food, came the presents. Renata was awestruck at the wrapped gifts sitting on the floor. She ripped the paper off her own gift, tugged open the cardboard box and pulled out a crimson musical box. When she wound it up the music played as a clown swayed to and fro. She was overjoyed. She hugged Cilla and Edmund and kissed them affectionately on their cheeks.

Cilla told Renata she would receive a small gift each of the eight days. Renata was buzzing from the celebrations and could not contain her joy and excitement for the week ahead.

Later, Cilla gazed in awe at the gently flickering flame of the first night's candle on the *Menorah*. The flame could be so easily extinguished by a single breath yet instantly rekindled by the flame of another candle. This simple thought symbolised something much greater and more powerful to her. Renata was Cilla's flame. Renata's love for her mother had been extinguished though in time this love, she hoped, would be once again rekindled and shine brightly like the glowing flame of the *Chanukah* candle.

As the week of *Chanukah* advanced Renata went to bed exhausted from the excitement and fun – but not before she had said her bedtime prayers. Since Renata started the *Shema* nearly eight weeks previously she had progressed very well. She pronounced and remembered the Hebrew words perfectly.

So much so that on day seven of the festival she had finally memorised the entire Jewish bedtime prayer.

On that night Renata said her Christian bedtime prayer followed by a perfect recital of the *Shema*. Cilla looked on in awe. This day has seemed long coming a few months ago.

"Well done! That was beautiful," said Cilla.

"Thank you."

"Good night darling, I love you,"

"Good night."

The next day was the eighth and last day of *Chanukah*. All eight *Menorah* lights gleamed brightly, their yellow flames flickering intently. The family celebrated with song and food. The smiles were more radiant and warm. It had been a week of festivity in freedom.

Renata went up to bed exhausted but happy. She was in her pyjamas and ready for bed. Cilla braced herself.

"Darling, I am so proud of how well you have learnt the *Shema*."

"Thank you."

"You know, I was thinking ... umm ... you don't really need to say two prayers before bedtime anymore."

Renata looked up expectantly.

"One is actually enough ... umm ... you have learnt the *Shema* so beautifully. Why don't you just say the *Shema* now?"

"For today you mean?"

"For today, for tomorrow, let's see."

"Are you sure I don't need to say *Our Father* too?"

"Absolutely sure."

And so on the eighth day of the festival of lights the little girl finally recited the Jewish bedtime prayer. One prayer before bedtime.

Cilla tucked her in and kissed her on the forehead lovingly.

"Good night darling, I love you,"

"Good night. I love you too."

Cilla trembled. Did she just hear right? Had her daughter just said, "I love you?"

Yes, I think she did. Yes, she did. Cilla sat on the bedside, her heart pounding.

"This is my miracle. My princess has finally come home."

1946

By 1946 the sheer enormity of the destruction of world Jewry had come to light.

Because of the Nazi's efficient record keeping there were endless lists of names, dates and places of those who had been murdered. Letters confirming this information, where known, was sent by the Red Cross to surviving relatives.

Of the 140,000 Jews who lived in the Netherlands before the war, an estimated 100,000 were murdered.

And what of those beautiful children who had escaped the Schouwburg Theatre and with whom Cilla and Edmund had shared a hiding place? They were sent to another hiding place but were eventually betrayed by a Nazi sympathiser. After fifteen months in hiding, in the summer of 1944, they were found and herded onto one of the last trains bound for Auschwitz Birkenau from Westerbork.

The children – Anton, by then ten years old, eight-year-old Abram, seven-year-old twins Eliza and David, six-year-old

Silvia, and five-year-old Felix – all alone in the world, were all murdered in the gas chambers. As for Henriëtte Pimentel and Walter Süsskind, who had saved hundreds of children from the crèche opposite the Hollandsche Schouwburg Theatre – they too were murdered in the Auschwitz gas chambers.

And what about her close friend Paula, and her husband Michael? Their so called exemptions from deportation did not protect them or other employees of the Jewish Council. In the end they were all sent to their deaths. Michael was shot dead in his own kitchen in April 1943 as he tried to escape from the *Sipo* officers (security police) who came to arrest him. Paula jumped out of the balcony and escaped into hiding for the remainder of the war. But she was a broken woman forever.

The statistics were sickening. The first train from Westerbork departed on the 15 July 1942 carrying 1,135 Jews. Destination Auschwitz Birkenau.

The deportations were organised from Berlin, stating the date, destination and number of deportees. The destination was predominantly to Auschwitz, but also to Bergen Belsen, Theresienstadt and Sobibor.

In total nearly 107,000 people were deported from Westerbork on almost 100 transports, like lambs to the slaughter.

The last train – Transport XXIV/7 – left Westerbork on 4 September 1944, carrying over two thousand Jewish people to Theresienstadt, Czechoslovakia.

By 1946 Edmund found out that most of his large family had been killed. His father Shaul had died, probably in Majdanek in 1942, his brother Yossel had died in Auschwitz on the 30 May

1942, his sister Beile Freide had died in Majdanek in 1942, along with her husband and young child. His uncle Pinkus Friedmann, who had lived in Amsterdam, had been killed in Auschwitz. His father's brother Meir, his wife Yocheved and their seven daughters were all murdered. His father's other brother Itshe, his wife Leah and six out of their seven children were killed. Only one child Menachem Yechezkel survived as he hid as a non-Jew with Slovak partisans.

Cilla eventually received the letter she had quietly expected all along. Her father, Chaim David Schiff, born 10 October 1885 in Gorlice, Poland, had perished in the Sobibor extermination camp in Poland on Friday 4 June 1943, aged fifty seven. Her step-mother, Maria Schiff, had met the same fate.

The train carrying Chaim and Maria Schiff had left from Westerbork on Tuesday 1 June 1943, carrying 3,006 deportees. The three-day journey in cramped cattle trucks was worsened by terrible thirst, hunger, horror and finally, despair. The train passed through Germany, via Bremen, Berlin and Breslau before it reached Sobibor. Only one person was known to have survived this transport. The remaining 3,005 were sent to the gas chambers.

An estimated 250,000 Jewish souls were murdered at Sobibor. Less than twenty Dutch people were known to have survived this extermination camp. As with all the Nazi extermination camps, the victims were thrown into mass graves and their memories obliterated – no trace of them having ever existed as individuals. Many years later, one engraved metal identification tag was found at Sobibor. It bore the name of Lea Judith de la Penha, a six-year-old Jewish girl from Holland.

On reading the Red Cross letter about her father Cilla, the

normally calm, composed mother and wife, broke down. She collapsed, howling loudly and uncontrollably. Edmund tried to compose her but she wanted no comfort.

Later that night she looked at the diary she had kept during the war. Where was she on 4 June 1943 when her father had perished? "In hiding with the poor Schouwburg Children." She remembered now – it had been the lowest point of her life. It all made sense.

The tragic fate of the Biermans closest family members would haunt the couple at night and stay with them for the rest of their lives.

A few days after receiving the letter Cilla realised there was something she had to do. She set off soberly to her father's home on Nieuwe Kerkstraat with the spare set of keys she had always carried with her. She had not been back since 1942, when they had gone into hiding. Some instinct forbade her to return to his home as long as she did not know with absolute certainty that he had died. Cilla trembled as she unlocked the front door and stepped into the shop on the left hand side of the house. A veil of dust covered the counters; the shelves were still partially stocked with old packets of biscuits. On the top shelf stood the large biscuit tin, the one from which Anton was always invited to choose a special biscuit. Cilla remembered the twinkle in her father's eyes as he ran to meet her and scoop his grandson out of his pram.

Slowly scanning the room, Cilla's eyes settled on the white object hanging on the wall. Her father's starched work coat. She walked over, picked it up and pressed her face in its stiff, musty folds.

Much later she left, with the white coat in her hand, unable to look through the rest of the house. She would ask Edmund to pack up his belongings. She locked the door promising never to return. Back home, she hung the precious coat in the left hand corner of her wardrobe, out of sight but always there.

CHAPTER THIRTY

13 September 1947

C illa was now approaching her mid-thirties. The young woman was slowly transforming into a comfortable, middle-aged wife and mother. Anton was ten, a bright boy on the verge of adolescence, Renata a playful six-year-old.

The new family house gradually became "home" as the parents added small luxuries that had seemed incredible or impossible during the dark war years and their immediate aftermath. As in old times, a card table sat by the window. Once again they enjoyed playing cards with friends. Cilla's friend Pepi, whose husband had died after liberation from typhoid fever, had recently remarried. Cilla was happy she had met George and that she could rebuild a new life after her traumatic war experiences.

In the corner of the room stood a glass cabinet that filled up slowly as the years passed. On the middle shelf stood their most precious possession – a pair of ornate candle sticks, beside a smaller, simpler pair. The ornate Sabbath candle sticks, a gift from Cilla's long gone mother-in-law, were the symbol of past, present and future.

Edmund had set up an independent furrier business from the second floor of their house. Cilla resumed her life as a mother and homemaker, with a passionate intensity born of the lost war years. In her spare time she helped in the business and did a lot of voluntary work including visiting patients at the nearby psychiatric or general hospital. She was always on the look out to help whoever was in need.

Being a mother was something that came so naturally to her. Loving her children was a role she was born to do no matter how grief stricken she still felt two years after the end of the war. That feeling would never go away. The time did not diminish the intense sorrow she felt towards her long gone beloved father. She thought about him very often.

So many members of their two families had perished during those few years of madness that every moment of their lives, every contact with their children, surviving relatives and friends, was precious, a blessing not to be taken for granted.

But recently, they had lost close contact with the Resnels. Initially, they had visited the Biermans frequently for Sabbath meals and festivals. They had an open invitation and Cilla encouraged them to join the family. Grateful that they had been Renata's sole family in the war, Cilla considered them part of her family now. However, in the last few months there had barely been any contact. The last time they had seen each other was six months ago. It saddened Cilla although she understood how painful it must have been for them to see Renata grow up and not be part of their lives anymore. She understood that the visits probably upset them. Maybe she could encourage them to come over. She would call them tomorrow.

Life was as normal as it could be but it was far from easy and it was always fraught with emotion. Sometimes, in the middle of the night, Cilla would wake from a dreadful dream in which she wandered through the streets of Amsterdam, forlornly seeking her vanished children and her father. On these occasions she would awake, streaming with sweat, her heart racing, confused and wondering if her hiding place had been discovered. Every time this happened she sprang out of bed and checked on her children in their bedrooms. When she found them sleeping soundly she returned to her bed so grateful she had been blessed with their return.

The dreams had been particularly vivid the year before – throughout the almost year-long Nuremberg Trials of the major Nazi war criminals for crimes against humanity. The horrific atrocities carried out by the Nazis against the Jews were revealed through film and newspaper reports, opening up old wounds and torturing those survivors who had tried so hard to move on with their lives.

Arthur Seyss-Inquart, who had been Reich Commissioner for the German-occupied Netherlands from 1940-1945, was one of ten war criminals to be executed. He was hanged on 16 October 1946.

The Trials listed in terrible detail the nature and extent of each criminal's involvement. The Nazis had perpetrated mass murder throughout Europe and Russia, their poisoned tentacles reaching out to the smallest village as well as the greatest city. Everywhere, Jews had been rounded up and killed, in city squares or in forests, or transported to concentration camps where they were either murdered on arrival or worked to death. At Auschwitz alone up to 12,000 Jews a day had been gassed.

In 1941, British Prime Minister Winston Churchill said in the House of Commons, "We are in the presence of a crime without a name". That crime was later to become known as the Holocaust. The Nuremberg Trials exposed the main perpetrators, from those who planned the train timetables to those who ordered the shipments of Zyklon B gas and those who ran the concentration camps with military precision. Estimates of the numbers of murder victims were still vague but already ran into the millions. By the early 1950s, Cilla had learned that the true figure was in the region of six million Jews. Around a million gypsies had also been murdered, along with many political and religious opponents of the Nazis.

But Cilla couldn't relate to one huge number, a row of meaningless noughts. No – for her it was one plus one, plus one, plus one ... each one unique, irreplaceable. It was the horrific murder of so many of their beloved family and of so very many old friends and acquaintances. Every day she saw in imagination the faces of those she and Edmund had loved, befriended or known. The very close family shadowed her thoughts constantly:

***

- *Cilla's father Chaim Schiff*
- *Her step-mother Maria Schiff*
- *Edmund's father Shaul Bitterman*
- *His brother Yossel Bitterman*
- *His sister Beile Freide Bitterman and her husband and child*
- *His uncle and aunt Meir and Yocheved Bitterman*

*** Real names of family members that were murdered in the Holocaust.

- *His seven first cousins – Sura Bayla Bitterman and her six sisters*
- *His uncle and aunt Itshe and Leah Bitterman and six of their seven children, his first cousins:-*
- *Draizel Bitterman*
- *Binyomin Zev Wolf Bitterman*
- *Yehuda Yidl Bitterman*
- *Sura Rivka Bitterman*
- *Shmil Bitterman*
- *Devora Bitterman*
- *His uncle Pinkus Friedmann*

And hundreds of others who had once been part of Cilla's life: other cousins, good friends, friendly acquaintances, people she had talked to, waved at, smiled at, acknowledged in the street or simply just known – parents, children, neighbours, synagogue members, the baker, the butcher, the violinist, the actor, the policeman, the postman, the nursery teacher, the bus driver, the hat-maker, the dress-maker ... The list of names ran on like a river, into an endless sea of sorrow. They had just vanished off the face of the earth.

The reminders were always there – a man without his wife, a wife without her husband, parents without children, children without parents, a child without anyone. Empty seats, empty homes, empty souls. The signs were always there – especially in the summer when the dark inky blue death numbers were exposed on the arms of the Auschwitz survivors, recalling the unimaginable cold-blooded horror of a regime that turned people into numbers.

Cilla pushed the dark thoughts to the back of her mind as much as possible. Her family was now her whole world.

Yet she dared not close her eyes when she rested during the day. Even the shortest nap brought flashbacks: her father's special, sweet smile. Questions burned within her. How much did he suffer, on the train to Sobibor, at the death camp? No matter how much she tried to crush these thoughts they always surged back, the past overwhelming the present.

She was resting in the armchair one Sabbath afternoon in September, tired after another busy week, a lemon tea and slice of cake on the coffee table beside her. She was pondering the menu and preparations for the big meal the following evening – the Jewish New Year.

Renata was balanced cheerfully on her father's lap, eating a banana. Opposite her, Anton was curled up on the sofa, deep into a book. The doorbell rang suddenly. Cilla looked up. She was not expecting anyone in particular this afternoon, although friends were known to drop by unannounced. Renata jumped up and ran to the door, closely followed by Kees, wagging his tail in a flurry of excitement.

On the doorstep stood a couple – a quiet, modest, smiling middle-aged man and woman. The woman was clutching tightly a bundle wrapped in swathes of pale pink blanket.

The child looked up at the woman's face and then at the man's and broke into a beaming smile.

"Renata," said the woman, "how are you my dear?

At that moment Cilla appeared at the door. She gazed at the couple – and put her hand to her mouth in delighted shock. Valerie and Arnold Resnel and a bundle in a pink blanket. After twenty two years of marriage the couple had been finally blessed with a baby girl. Tears sprang to Cilla's eyes. She hugged Arnold tightly and turned to Valerie, who tenderly handed the baby to her husband. The two women embraced tightly. The tears of both made words unnecessary. Cilla then lifted the bundle out of Arnold's hands and lovingly cradled the tiny baby in her arms.

"Thank you ... oh, thank you for coming to tell us ... What a beautiful, beautiful baby. What's her name?"

"Her name? Her name ... it's ... Renata."

AFTERWORD

by Renata (Bitterman) Matyas, 2014

ow lucky was I to dance the night away with my parents
at my wedding. I look back in wonder at the treasured,
slightly fading photograph from that day – 17 July 1962.
I was a twenty-one-year-old bride dancing with my mother and
father. My new husband, Yisachaar Matyas, is sitting to the left,
transfixed, his father Yechezkel, standing on the far right, looking
on.

How lucky was I to be dancing with my beloved father and
mother. How lucky were they to be dancing with me? After all

that had happened – it was a miracle.

And on that day, seventeen years after the war had ended, Vie and Aart Versnel were honoured guests with their two lovely daughters. Their gift to me was a silver dish engraved: "To Renata: from your beloved foster parents." My gratitude to them for risking their lives in sheltering me during the war and for their unfailing, unconditional love is beyond words.

My mother gave us the best childhood possible in post-war Amsterdam, filled with outdoor sports – walking, cycling, tennis. With us she was a happy, smiling, perfect mother who doted on us. She was the perfect hostess and friend: our home was always filled with guests, playing cards and games or joining us for tea.

After the war we spent many care-free summers in a rented house by the sea in Scheveningen. We soaked in the sun, swam in the sea and looked forward to our weekly order of fresh fish every Thursday evening.

She never spoke of her years in hiding, her trauma, her loss or her sadness. She saved that for her private moments.

She told me once that one of her favourite memories was sitting behind me on my bike, her arms around my waist, as I cycled in Bilthoven one summer's day. That too is one of my favourite memories.

My beautiful mother lived to see me get married. She adored Yisachaar and he was so close to her. She lived to see the birth of her four beautiful grand-daughters – my daughters Miriam, Nadine and Jackie as well as Arthur's daughter Nathalie.

She suffered uncomplaining from the terrible colitis that had afflicted her for many years, exacerbated by the tulip bulbs she was forced to eat during the Hunger Winter of 1944-5. She died from the illness on 17 July 1974, aged sixty-one, on my twelfth wedding anniversary, exactly forty years ago. She was still in the prime of her life, when she should have finally been able to sit back and enjoy all she had achieved.

As I look back at her life and suffering, I am more than ever awed by her courage, determination and strength. Not a day has gone by in the last forty years that I have not thought about my beloved mother, my best friend and mentor, who contributed so much to our lives. I am so very grateful to my daughter Nadine for honouring her memory through this story.

I think my mother would be so proud of the legacy she left: the legacy that nearly never was, that lives on in the lives of her four grand-daughters and fifteen great grand-children.

Renata (Bitterman) Matyas

The True Story in Pictures of
Cilli and Eugen Bitterman and their family

(to be looked at after you have read the story)

Before the War

Parents of Eugen: Sura-Raisel and Shaul Bitterman.
Sura-Raisel (maiden name Weinfeld), died 1938 Spisske Podhradie,
Czechoslovakia (now Slovakia). Shaul Bitterman, born 1884 in
Stara Lubovna, Czechoslovakia. He was deported on 29 May 1942.
He was murdered possibly in Majdanek concentration camp, Poland,
1942.

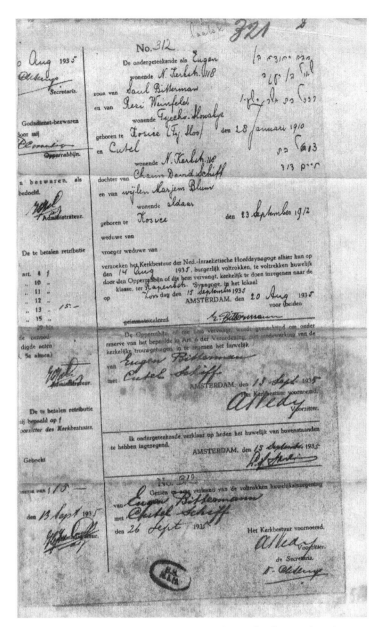

September 1935, Amsterdam. Marriage certificate of Cilli (Cutel) and Eugen
Bitterman.

1938, Visiting Eugen's Family, Spisske Podhradie, Czechoslovakia.
Front row, left to right: Cilli and Eugen holding their baby son Arthur, sister-in-law Pearl and Eugen's brother Usher holding their baby daughter Gittele.
Back row: Eugen's brother Shia and sister Beile Freide.

1938, Spisske Podhradie, Eugen's brothers with their grandfather Yaakov.
Left to right: Shia, Yossel (Josef), Yaakov, Usher Bitterman.

1938, Spisske Podhradie.
Bitterman sisters-in-law; Cilli, Pearl and Beile Freide.
Eugen's sister Beile Freide was murdered in Majdanek in 1942, along with her husband and young child.

Page of Testimony · דף עד

Page of Testimony for commemoration of the Jews who perished during the Holocaust, please fill in a separate form for each victim, in black capitals

		Victim's family name: שם משפחה של הנספה
Victim's photo. Please write victim's name on back. Do not glue.	Maiden name:	BITTERMAN
	Previously/born family name: שם משפחה קודם/מולדת	First name (also nickname): שם פרטי (גם שם חיבה/כינוי) JOSEF
Approx. age at death: גיל משוער בעת המוות 28	Date of birth: תאריך לידה 1974	Gender: מין M/F Title: תואר MR.
Nationality: לאום CZECHOSLOVAK	Country: ארץ CZECHOSLOVAKIA	Region: מחוז SPIS	Place of birth: מקום לידה SPISSKE PODHRADIA
Victim's family name: father: שם משפחה אב BITTERMAN		First name: שם פרטי SAUL	
Victim's family name: mother: שם משפחה אם WEINFELD	Maiden name: שם לפני הנישואין	First name: שם פרטי SURE RAISEL	
Victim's wife/husband: Sex of children מין הילדים SINGLE	Family status משפחתי	Maiden name: שם לפני הנישואין	First name: שם פרטי	Permanent residence: מקום מגורים קבוע
Address:		Country: ארץ	Region: מחוז	
Member of any movement: חבר באיזו תנועה/ארגון	Place of work: מקום העבודה		Profession: מקצוע	
Address:		Country: ארץ	Region: מחוז	Residence before deportation: מגורים לפני הגירוש
Date of death: תאריך המוות 1942	Country: ארץ POLAND	Region: מחוז	Place of death: מקום המוות MAJDANEK
Circumstances of death: נסיבות המוות				

Yad Vashem Archive: Eugen's brother Yossel (Josef) born 10 April 1914, was murdered in Majdanek Concentration Camp in 1942, aged twenty-eight years old.

24 Plantage Parklaan, Amsterdam: Family Bitterman's home before they went into hiding.

Amsterdam 1942. Before going into hiding. Renata with her mother Cilli and father Eugen. Later Renata and Arthur go into separate hiding places. Cilli and Eugen go into hiding together.

Hollandsche Schouwburg: Formerly a theatre, the building, situated around the corner from Cilli and Eugen Bitterman's home, was used to round up Jews before deporting them to concentration camps. Today it is a national Holocaust Museum.

Archive record of Cilli's father Chaim David Schiff. Born 10 October 1885, Gorlice, Poland. He was murdered with his wife Maria Schiff on 4 June 1943 in Sobibor extermination camp, Poland.

After the War

Cilli and Eugen are reunited with their children Renata and Arthur after the war.

Having been brought up by a Christian couple during her time in hiding Renata came back home reciting Christian prayers. Her mother Cilli patiently waited for her young daughter to be well integrated in her new life before she taught her the Jewish prayers again.

24 Sarphatistraat, Amsterdam: Home to the Bitterman family after the war.

Renata with her dog Kees.

Amsterdam 1950. *Left to right:* Shia and (standing behind him) his wife Fay Bitterman, Arthur, Renata, Cilli and Eugen.

Vie and Aart Versnel – who courageously hid Renata Bitterman.

After the war, following twenty-two years of marriage, the couple had their first daughter whom they named Renata. A few years later another daughter was born.

Versnel and Bitterman Family Reunion circa 1960.
Back row, left to right: Aart and Vie Versnel, Renata, Cilli.

Amsterdam 1962. Engagement of Renata Bitterman to Yisachaar Matyas.
Left to right: Yechezkel, Sarah and Yisachaar Matyas, Renata, Cilli and Eugen Bitterman.

Wedding of Renata Bitterman to Yisachaar Matyas:
Jacob Obrechtstraat Synagogue, Amsterdam, 17 July 1962

Vie Versnel with Aart and their two daughters come to congratulate Renata at her wedding. Their gift was a silver dish engraved:

"To Renata from your beloved foster parents".

Amsterdam, 1962. *Left to right:* Renata's cousin Leiby (Robert)
Bitterman, Fay and her son Sholi, Leiby's wife Rebecca.

1967, Eugen and Cilli's first grandchild, Miriam Michelle
Matyas.

London, 1974. Renata with her daughters. *Left to right:* Nadine, Jackie, Miriam.

London 1974. *Left to right:* Cilli, with her grandchildren and daughter, Miriam, Jackie, Renata, Nadine.

24 Sarphatistraat, Amsterdam 2009.
Nadine with her mother Renata visiting the childhood
home she lived in after the war, (now converted to a
nursery).

Renata and Yisachaar with their daughters, 2013. *Left to right:* Nadine, Renata, Miriam, Yisachaar, Jackie.

Saving one person, 2013. Renata and Yisachaar with all their children and grandchildren.

The Bitterman Family Tree

Compiled by Rebecca Bitterman

Children of Yaacov and Sura Baile Bitterman
Meir, Tzvi Hersh, Leibish, Itshe and Shaul (father of Eugen)

Grandparents of Eugen Bitterman
Yaacov Bitterman *m* Sura Baile
Mandel.

Shaul Bitterman
b 1884 in Stara Lubovna. Deported
on 29 May 1942, murdered possibly
in Majdanek (20 Sivan)..

m. Reza, Sura Raisel [Rosalie] Weinfeld
d. Spisske Podhradie, 1938 (19 Nissan)

Grandfather of Sure Raisel Weinfeld
Josef Weinfeld.

Children of Shaul and Sura Raisel Bitterman

Parents of Sura Raisel Weinfeld
Usher Yeshaya Weinfeld, Bocharov, *m.* Gitel Avraham.

Sura Reisel Weinfeld's siblings
Rachel, Shmuel, Malka, Joshua, Beile, Chana. (Rachel Weinfeld
b.03.09.1889. *d.* 3 Mar.1940 buried in Diemen *m.* Pinkus Friedmann.)

Children
Katherine *b.* 25 Jan 1937
Robert (Leiby*) *b.* 16 Sep 1938
Ruth *b.* 2 June 1941

Ascher Usher Yeshaya, known as Usher, *b.* 3 Sept
1908 in Kosice, *d.* 28 Sep 1974. *m.* 24 Feb 1936 ——— Edouard (Shalom) *b.* 22 Sep 1945
Pearl Schwartz *b.* 11 Jan 1910 in Kosice *d.* 24 June
1983

Elliot *b.* 21 Jan 1949.
*Leiby *m.* Rebecca Krzywanowski, 19 Dec
1961 who compiled this Family Tree. Their
children are Joshua, Naomi and Miriam.

Eugen, Yehuda, (Yidl) *b.* 28 Jan 1910, Kosice
d. 1994 Antwerp *m.* Cilli (Cutel Tzurtel Schiff)
b. 23 Sept 1912, Kosice, *d.* 17 July 1974, Amsterdam.

Cilli's mother was Marjem Blum.
Her father was Chaim Dovid Schiff,
Josef, (Jossel) *b.* 10 April   (descendants of the Rebbe Elimelech of
1914. *d.* 30 May 1942, (20   Lizhensk). *b.* 10 Oct 1885, Gorlice, *d.*
Sivan), Auschwitz   4 June 1943 Sobibor with second wife,
Maria Schiff Weinberger, *b.* 13 Aug,
Bardejov.

Eugen and Cilli *m.* 15 Sept 1935,
Rapenburg Synagogue Amsterdam

Belle Freide *b.* Spisske
Podhradie[Kirdorf] CZ.
m with child. Murdered,
Majdanek 1942 (20 Sivan).

Children
Arthur, Elazar *b.* 20 Feb 1937 *m.* Lola Latasch,
Germany, 3 Feb 1968
Renata Raisel *b.* 6 Feb 1941, Amsterdam *m.* Yisachaar
Matyas, Romania, 17 July 1962, Amsterdam,

Emanuel, Menachem Joshua,
known as Shia. *b.* 1918 *d.*
2007, Antwerp *m.* Fanny,   *Grandchildren of Cilli & Eugen Bitterman*
Feigele (Fay) Tannenbaum,   Nathalie Simona Deborah Bitterman
born 1925, London. *m.* 7 Sep   Miriam Michelle Matyas
1943 in London   Nadine Chaya Matyas
Jackie Esther Matyas

Children
Shaul *b.* Mar 1959, Tel-Aviv

The grandchildren and great-grandchildren
of Cilli & Eugen Bitterman

Miriam Matyas m. *Tzachi Even-Ari 27 Dec 1989*

Raquel Cilla *b*. 1 Jan 1991
Sylvie Chava *b*. 9 July 1992
Daniel Yehuda *b*. 8 Jan 1996
Benny Yechezkel *b*. 21 Sep 1998
David Yoseph *b*. 28 Oct 2000
Raphael Chaim *b*. 1 Nov 2006

Nadine Matyas m. *Oded Wojakovski 29 Sep 1994*

Nathalie Dina *b*. 24 Dec 1997
Nicole Chava *b*.21 Sep 1999
Alex Yehuda *b*. 5 Mar 2005

Jackie Matyas m. *Jeremy Benjamin 24 Aug 1997*

Emmanuelle Tzila Mazal-Tov *b*. 25 Nov 1999
Ethan Yechezkel *b*. 26 Mar 2002
Sasha Simcha *b*. 26 Sep 2003
Eliana, Chava *b*. 24 Nov 2009

Nathalie Bitterman m. *Avi Chekroun 27 Dec 2000*

Anthony David *b*. 15 Nov 2001
Tiffany Tsila *b*. 15 Nov 2004

Made in the USA
Middletown, DE
18 February 2015